RHS
How Do
WORMS
WORK?

RHS How Do Worms Work?
Author: Guy Barter
First published in Great Britain in 2016 by Mitchell Beazley,
a division of Octopus Publishing Group Ltd,
Carmelite House, 50 Victoria Embankment, London EC4Y 0DZ
www.octopusbooks.co.uk

An Hachette UK Company
www.hachette.co.uk

Published in association with the Royal Horticultural Society
Copyright © Quid Publishing 2016
Text copyright © Quid Publishing 2016
ISBN: 978 1 78472 228 9

A CIP catalogue record of this book is available from the British Library
Set in Archer and Open Sans
Printed and bound in China

Mitchell Beazley Publisher: Alison Starling
RHS Publisher: Rae Spencer-Jones
RHS Consultant Editor: Simon Maughan

Conceived, designed and produced by
Quid Publishing, Part of the Quarto Group
Ovest House
58 West Street
Brighton
BN1 2RA
England
Design: Lindsey Johns
With thanks to Sophie Collins, Simon Akeroyd, Holly Farrell and Matthew Biggs

The Royal Horticultural Society is the UK's leading gardening charity
dedicated to advancing horticulture and promoting good gardening.
Its charitable work includes providing expert advice and information,
training the next generation of gardeners, creating hands-on opportunities
for children to grow plants and conducting research into plants, pests
and environmental issues affecting gardeners.

For more information visit www.rhs.org.uk or call 0845 130 4646.

RHS
How Do
WORMS
WORK?

A GARDENER'S COLLECTION
of Curious Questions
and Astonishing Answers

GUY BARTER
RHS CHIEF HORTICULTURAL ADVISOR

MITCHELL
BEAZLEY

Contents

4 Weather, Climate and the Seasons

5 In the Garden

■ Introduction

Do you really need to know how worms work?

And if you do, will it make you a better gardener? I've run an advice service for gardeners for over two decades – first with *Gardening Which?* and subsequently for the Royal Horticultural Society – and I'd answer 'yes' to both questions. When you're gardening, while your hands are busy digging, planting, weeding and pruning, your brain is free to wander. Most gardeners find that a constant stream of questions runs through their minds as they work. Some may be practical, others are whimsical, and many aren't easily answered without full knowledge of a whole range of subjects, from soil structure to plant chemistry.

Garden revelations

How Do Worms Work? offers accessible, in-depth answers to 130 of those not-so-incidental questions. And while they might not all have an immediate, obvious application to practical gardening, you'll find that they build your gardening knowledge without you even noticing – giving you a useful bank of facts that you'll be drawing on for years to come. Among other things, we'll tell you why it is that one plant is always visited by bees while another seems to attract only butterflies. And how much space tree roots really take up (and whether they could possibly make your house collapse). And how on earth different soils can actually make some flowers change colour... And much, much more. Gardens are where you meet nature close up: plants, insects, soil all have their own ways of working, both in isolation and in cooperation with other elements, so there's a lot going on in even the smallest of spaces.

◀ Hydrangeas are arguably the finest summer shrubs, but their colour depends on soil conditions. Knowing the basis for blue or pink helps get good results.

The more you learn, the clearer your picture of the community on your back doorstep will be, and the better you will understand how its different parts work, from the worms in the soil to the leaves up above and all the levels in between.

It's a jungle out there

Not everything in the garden is rosy. The sometimes shocking revelations you'll find in *How Do Worms Work?* ensure that you'll look at your garden – or any other cultivated space – with a completely fresh eye. On the surface, your plot may look calm, domestic, perhaps even suburban, but if you don't believe that nature is red in tooth and claw, some of what you find in the following pages will make you change your mind. (By the way, did you know that slugs have teeth on their tongues? No wonder they make you shudder.) Below the soil is the perpetual sound of faint crunching as millions of tiny organisms consume millions of even smaller ones; above it, plants get to

▲ Bleeding heart, *Lamprocapnos spectabilis*, was formerly officially called *Dicentra spectabilis*. Name changes are less irksome if you know the botany behind plant names.

work in chemical labs of mind-boggling complexity to ensure that their flowers are the brightest and their scents the smelliest – enough to outshine and out-scent their rivals in the competition to attract their insect admirers. Reproduction is the name of the game, and the ruthless inhabitants of your garden will adopt any tactics to achieve it.

Arm yourself with *How Do Worms Work?* and you'll find any garden a richer, more dynamic, more engrossing place to be. Not only that, but you're guaranteed to improve your gardening skills without even trying.

A QUICK ANSWERS

The 'A' box under each question offers you the quick and dirty answer in the shortest form possible. Read on for the main text, which offers additional context and plenty of extra detail.

Chapter 1

Seeds and Plants

Why are trees so big?

LIFE IS AS MUCH A STRUGGLE FOR PLANTS as for others, and the bigger the plant the more likely it is to overcome its competitors and come out on top. By casting shade, and to a much lesser extent hogging water and nutrients, trees suppress other vegetation.

If a garden is abandoned, first annual weeds will cover the ground, then grasses and perennial weeds, followed by brambles. After that, small pioneer trees such as ash, *Fraxinus*, birch, *Betula*, maple, *Acer*, mountain ash, *Sorbus aucuparia*, pine, *Pinus*, sycamore, *Acer pseudoplatanus*, and willow, *Salix*, will start to appear. Pioneer species are often relatively short-lived (80 years or so). As they fall, larger trees will come to dominate: beech, *Fagus*, lime, *Tilia*, and oak, *Quercus*, for example. It may take hundreds of years for these 'climax vegetation' trees to reach their ultimate height before beginning a long period of decline. In gardens it is the smaller pioneer trees that are particularly valued – birch, maples and willows being widely cultivated. The giants are best restricted to parks and forestry.

Room to grow

Trees to the general observer are big things that cast shade and have a single stem from which branches radiate usually at some distance above the ground. However, size is only possible where water and nutrients are available so that arid regions

◀ There must also be a genetic component that also limits the height of trees. No matter how much you water an oak tree (far left) it will never match the loftiness of a Californian redwood, *Sequoia sempervirens* (left).

A By growing tall, trees literally put shrubs and other plants in the shade, ensuring their success by outgrowing their competitors for light.

and rocky or mountainous parts are populated by lesser plants – grasses, shrubs, low growing plants – that cling to the soil surface and by bulbs, corms and tubers.

WHERE TO PLANT A TREE

Some soils, particularly clays, shrink as they dry. In summer, trees extract water and soils shrink. Winter rains restore soil moisture, but although the soil swells again it does not always restore the soil to its original volume. Soil shrinkage accumulates over time, potentially causing damage to nearby buildings. Ideally, you should avoid planting trees close to buildings, and strengthen foundations when building near existing trees.

And why no bigger?

The taller the tree the greater the exposure to wind damage and more leverage on the lower parts. To strengthen the lower trunk and base of boughs the tree has to invest as much as eight times as much timber as near the top or bough extremities. At some stage the investment in timber outweighs the benefits and it is no longer 'profitable' for trees to get taller even though by doing so they would shade the competition. This limit is more quickly reached in windy Europe than in calmer Californian valleys, for example.

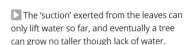

▶ The 'suction' exerted from the leaves can only lift water so far, and eventually a tree can grow no taller though lack of water.

Is lichen a plant?

LICHENS ARE EXTRAORDINARY STRUCTURES, consisting of a mutually beneficial – symbiotic – partnership between an alga and a fungus. The two link to make a new structure, and the combination makes for an impressively tough result. Lichens thrive on unfriendly surfaces, such as bare brick or tree trunks, which would defeat less hardy organisms.

So what credentials does a true plant need to have? The dictionary definition of a plant, and the one that most people would recognise, is a living thing that grows in earth or water (or, sometimes, colonises other plants), that usually has stems, leaves, flowers and roots, and that reproduces by means of seeds. But it is a definition that leaves out a lot of the more unusual members of the family. The 'plant' group includes not only flowering plants (known as angiosperms) but also ferns and conifers (gymnosperms), and, much less recognisably to the uninformed eye, algae, mosses and liverworts, too.

Algae: the environment's flexible friends

Despite their simple structure, algae have an importance in the environment far beyond their symbiotic role in the formation of lichens. They play a crucial part in many different ecosystems.

The goblet-like structures of lichen are called podetia. They carry reproductive bodies and are typical of the Cladonia. Cladonia are very widespread, especially on tree trunks.

A Lichens are usually considered to be not-quite-plants, while algae are very simple plants. Fungi are a separate group from plants altogether: the marriage between the two makes for a hybrid that is not easily defined.

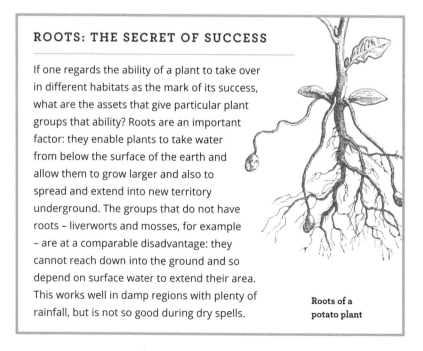

Diatoms are single-celled algae abundant in fresh and seawater. They perform up to 25 percent of global photosynthesis and are an important source of atmospheric oxygen.

Seaweeds, for example, are algae, and algae are abundant in both fresh and saltwater. In the ocean, tiny, free-floating algae are known as phytoplankton, and are responsible for more than half the photosynthesis on the planet, meaning that they are instrumental in producing the oxygen on which almost all life depends.

World rulers

In terms of widespread colonisation of habitat, flowering plants have the winning formula for growing and reproducing. Other groups lag behind this success: for example, a single flowering plant group, such as the Fabaceae (pea family) contains about 18,000 species, in contrast to the entire family of ferns which, while widespread in the world, boasts only about 12,000 types.

ROOTS: THE SECRET OF SUCCESS

If one regards the ability of a plant to take over in different habitats as the mark of its success, what are the assets that give particular plant groups that ability? Roots are an important factor: they enable plants to take water from below the surface of the earth and allow them to grow larger and also to spread and extend into new territory underground. The groups that do not have roots – liverworts and mosses, for example – are at a comparable disadvantage: they cannot reach down into the ground and so depend on surface water to extend their area. This works well in damp regions with plenty of rainfall, but is not so good during dry spells.

Roots of a potato plant

Q How many plant species are there?

THE IDEA OF ARRIVING AT A REALISTIC ESTIMATE of the number of plant species in the world is daunting. So it is not so surprising that even the experts disagree on the 'real' likely total.

On the one hand, The International Plant Names Index, which is a collaborative project undertaken between the Royal Botanic Gardens at Kew, the Herbarium at Harvard University and the Australian National Herbarium, and which is agreed internationally to be the definitive source, lists 1,642,517 plant names for 2016. What is more, the list is being augmented constantly: 1,560 new names were added in 2015 alone.

But all is not as it seems – the Index total (which incorporates flowering plants, seed plants, ferns and mosses) is widely agreed to be a huge overestimate, because so very many plants have more than one name.

PLANTING BY NUMBERS

If these numbers seem too vast to compute, you can take comfort in the mere 75,000 species found in the Royal Horticultural Society's online Plant Finder. What is more, they are all available for the gardener to buy and try in their own plot.

On the other hand, Kew Gardens and the Missouri Botanical Garden have together generated a second list, The Plant List, which includes plants with water-conducting vessels, flowering plants, conifers and ferns. It tops out at 350,000 accepted names.

Who is correct? The Plant List is probably closer to the real headcount – and since new plants are being discovered all the time, you could safely add an extra 50,000 and declare the total at a probable 400,000.

A There are probably

somewhere between 350,000 and more than 1.5 million plant species. That sounds very vague indeed, but there are reasons.

How are new plants made from pieces of other plants?

THE MOST FAMILIAR METHOD PLANTS USE to reproduce themselves is by setting seed, every seed having the potential to turn into a new plant. However, gardeners successfully take cuttings from many plant types, and some plants seem to be able to make new 'young' from the tiniest piece of the parent plant. You cannot make a new animal from a single body part, so how do plants do it?

The simplest way in which this skill manifests itself is when a part of a plant that has become separated from the main body takes root. In the garden, if you take the tiniest shoot of common mint (one of the most rampant opportunists of the plant world) and push it into the soil, it will almost always grow into a new plant. In the same way, some trees in wet areas – dogwood, *Cornus*, poplar, *Populus*, and willow, *Salix*, for example – will easily spread at times of flooding, as twigs are broken off, carried away, and then root elsewhere. Not every

Plant cells are not like animal cells – every one has the ability to recreate any part of its parent plant, rather than each cell only being able to create the plant part it originally comes from. The tongue-tying term for this is totipotecy.

plant finds it so easy. But a skill with cuttings is one of the hallmarks of a true gardener, and the basis of ornamental horticulture is the reproduction of desirable plants, which in some cases is actually easier to manage with cuttings than with seeds.

HORTICULTURAL MINI-MES

In modern plant science, microscopic plant fragments can be cultured in laboratories to produce dozens of tiny young, a process known as micropropagation.

▶ There are 25 species of mint and 196 garden forms are known. Nearly all spread by creeping roots, making them exceptionally easy to propagate.

How old is my tree?

WHILE IT IS EASY TO ESTABLISH HOW OLD A TREE IS if you fell it, it is far more of a challenge to find out its age without cutting it down, although there are one or two ways to get a broad idea.

Creating the rings

Every spring, as the growing season starts, a tree produces a new layer of cells around the periphery of its trunk. The cambium is the layer dividing the xylem and the phloem, the two kinds of tissue that act as the vascular, or circulatory, system of the tree. The cambium itself divides in two, the outer layer increasing the width of the phloem, and the inner layer joining the xylem cells to broaden the xylem layer.

The way to read a tree's age accurately is to take a cross-section of the trunk and count the number of rings you can see in it – each ring represents a year's growth.

▼ From the central seedling's pith to the peripheral growing cambium, a layer of wood has been deposited annually over decades and even centuries.

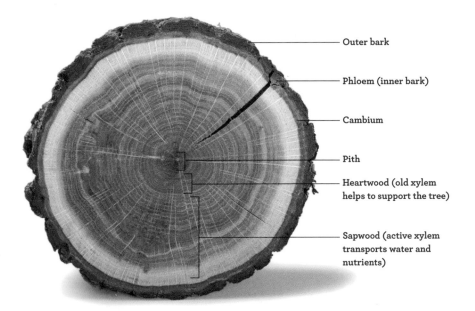

Outer bark

Phloem (inner bark)

Cambium

Pith

Heartwood (old xylem helps to support the tree)

Sapwood (active xylem transports water and nutrients)

Together, the two layers of new cells make a distinct, visible ring inside the tree's trunk – broader when the growing year has been a good one and the tree has put on more bulk; narrower when growing conditions have not been so favourable. And every year the process is repeated: count the rings when a mature tree is cut down, and you can age it exactly. What is more, the comparable width of the rings offer the informed tree reader, or dendrochronologist, a record of climate conditions across the tree's life.

AGEING A TREE WITHOUT CUTTING IT DOWN

Scientists at the Forestry Commission in the UK have estimated that if you measure the diameter of the trunk of a tree, you can find out how old it is by making a comparative study with the data of similarly sized trees. The disadvantage of this method is that you need a sizeable number of examples for comparison – it is not practical if you are trying to age just one or two specimens.

For the interested gardener, there is a simplified version you can try using a tape measure:

Younger tree = thinner trunk

• Measure the girth of the tree trunk in centimetres at a point 1m up from the ground.

• Then divide the girth by 2.5 to get an estimate of the tree's age

For example, a girth of 150cm would suggest the tree was approximately 60 years old.

Older tree = thicker trunk

Why are some leaves purple?

To us, the majority of leaves appear to be green when in full growth and this is because they are rich in chlorophyll – a substance that is attached to the membranes of the leaves and that absorbs blue and red light, but reflects green light strongly. When the leaves lose chlorophyll in autumn, the filter it offers is removed and we instead see the autumn leaves in shades of intense red and orange. So why do some leaves appear to us as a deep red or purple all year round?

Leaves that appear purple are the result of chance mutations; they contain high levels of anthocyanins, which are pigments that absorb green light and reflect reds and purples.

The smoke tree, *Cotinus coggygria* 'Royal purple', is an excellent, almost tree-like shrub (5m), with dark purple summer leaves and a red autumn colour.

Unlike chlorophyll, anthocyanins are present in the sap of leaves: they are the result of a reaction between sugars and proteins in the sap. In plants where they are strongly present, the colour created may be a rich purple. Anthocyanins do not seem to offer the parent plant any advantage, and red pigment is expensive for plants to produce in terms of energy. As a result, purple-leaved plants are slower growing than green ones, so in the wild they are at a disadvantage.

In cultivation, though, their rich hues are often valued by gardeners, and plants are bred to retain the strong colouring as truly as possible. If you are a purple-leaf enthusisast, two recent popular breeding successes are *Physocarpus opulifolius* 'Diabolo' and *Sambucus nigra* f. *porphyrophylla* 'Eva' – both deciduous, resilient, easy shrubs that make great substitutes for the beautiful but expensive purple-leaved Japanese acers, *Acer japonicum* and *A. palmatum*.

What is a seed?

SEEDS VARY SO MUCH IN APPEARANCE, from dust-like grains to pea-sized lumps, that it can be hard to accept that they all do the same job, yet every seed, small or large, shares the inherent capacity to create a brand-new plant.

We do not know the evolutionary path by which seeds originally developed. The earliest plants are thought to have reproduced by means of spores – single-cell units that are simpler than seeds, but with less individual chance of success. Gradually, seeds overtook them as plants developed, although some simple structures, such as algae and fungi, still rely on spores. Seeds cost the plant more to produce, but have more potential: larger seeds, in particular, produce large seedlings,

Essentially, a seed is a little package containing a miniature plant – root, shoot, one or two minute 'seed leaves' and a small amount of food to keep it going until the seedling can photosynthesise for itself.

which stand a much better chance of outcompeting other plants and of surviving the onslaughts of predators, such as slugs or beetles.

THE ART OF DISPERSAL

Not only are plants able to produce seeds, but many have also devised specialised ways to send them a fair distance from the parent. This is helpful, since it gradually extends the spread of each species. The legumes of the pea family have large seeds produced in pods which, when mature, explode, flicking the seeds a considerable distance. Tiny seeds are blown by the wind to new homes, while some hefty examples, such as acorns, rely on birds or animals to move them to fresh territory.

How do seeds know when to germinate?

GERMINATING AT AN ADVANTAGEOUS TIME is one of the key moments in the transformation of a seed into a seedling. If it is timed right, germination and subsequent growth will be fast and efficient; get it wrong, though, and germination may be the last thing the seed ever does.

Taking their time

Although seeds need to lie dormant, they also need to germinate within a certain period because they will lose viability over time (this is the reason for the 'sow by' dates you see on seed packets).

In northern areas, most plants produce their seeds abundantly in the later summer and autumn. They have a variety of mechanisms to inhibit germination until the most advantageous time for the cycle of their parent plant to begin. Some plants, particularly members of the pea and broom family, produce seeds with thick, hard, waterproof coats that need to be rotted by microorganisms in the soil. This can take more than one winter to accomplish, but eventually the coating will wear away and the seed will be able to germinate. Other plants produce specialised seeds with even harder casings; these are designed to be eaten by birds and to stay in the gizzard where grit is stored – gradually the grit will wear down some of the seedcase, and the bird

Seeds are pre-packaged plants with a root, two seed leaves and a tiny central shoot, which begin a new life after breaking free of the seed coat.

SUCCESS WITH PARSLEY

Parsley is notoriously hard to germinate. One traditional way to get it growing is to sow the seed, cover it with soil, then pour boiling water over the planted patch.

This method does actually have a basis in science: parsley seed has a water-soluble germination inhibitor in its tough coat.

will ultimately eject the seed so that it can germinate. Still other plants, beetroot among them, incorporate plant chemicals or hormones either in the seeds themselves or in the fruits that surround them. If the seed falls into wet soil, the chemical leaches out and the seed germinates, but, if it lands on dry ground, germination will not happen until the seed gets wet.

There are various artificial ways for the gardener to overcome a seed's natural dormancy and encourage germination. Some seeds with hard casings can be nicked with a sharp knife or lightly rubbed with sandpaper to wear them down; in the case of waterproof seeds, a soaking in hot water before sowing will help. Even those seeds that have adapted to be processed in a bird's gizzard can be given a false taste of the experience by being mixed with sharp sand and then ground between two boards. Commercial growers may even treat very tough seeds with sulphuric acid before planting, although you should not try this at home.

Seeds need to have a period of dormancy between being 'finished' by their parent plant and germinating. Many have evolved with some protection that ensures they remain dormant until the right time; in some cases, this consists of an outer coating that has to degrade before the seed begins to grow.

What makes herbs smell nice?

ALTHOUGH HUMANS USUALLY ENJOY THE SCENT OF HERBS, the compounds that create the different smells are not there to please people, but to protect the plants. Many plants smell, but not all the smells are agreeable to humans – just two examples are glory flower, *Clerodendrum bungei*, and beefsteak plant, *Perilla frutescens*, both of which – to our noses – smell of rotten meat.

Scent: the raw materials

We take scent in through a moist layer in the upper part of the nasal cavity called the olfactory epithelium. To be smelled, scent molecules need to be small, to evaporate at normal temperatures and to be soluble in oil. The molecules are collected on the olfactory epithelium, where they dissolve and pass over scent sensor cells that communicate directly with the brain, where the smell is then registered – that is the point at which you become consciously aware of a smell.

Herb plants undertake a complex biochemical process to make the compound molecules that create a scent. The purpose of the scent is to act as a deterrent or insecticide for particular, non-beneficial insects.

Each plant species creates its own mix of scent chemicals to make its own distinctive smell – the 'formula' of mint, *Mentha*, for example, contains menthol and methone, while the scent of lavender, *Lavandula*, is made up from 47 different compounds, chief amongst them the unappealingly named 1,5-Dimethyl-1-vinyl-4-hexenyl butyrate.

The oils that protect lavender, *Lavandula*, leaves from damaging heat and light make their essential oils useful as a scent, preservative and balm.

GROWING HIGHLY SCENTED HERBS

You can exploit herbs' natural tendencies in order to get the best scent and flavour from them.

They do best if they are not indulged – if you spoil them by giving them plenty of water and fertiliser and removing the threat of insect predators, they will reward you by producing less scent. Instead, offer a harder life with poor soil and sparse watering. They will fare better, too, outside a greenhouse, as sunlight encourages both good scent and flavour. And finally, if all else fails, you can indulge in some serious deception by using plant growth regulators – which you can buy in any nursery or online. These contain natural hormones that are 'read' by the plants as a pest attack, and that will stimulate them to greater efforts, resulting in a stronger scent and a better culinary flavour.

Peppermint,
Mentha × piperita

Rosemary,
Rosmarinus officinalis

Sage,
Salvia officinalis

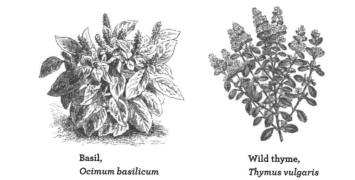

Basil,
Ocimum basilicum

Wild thyme,
Thymus vulgaris

When is a plant a weed?

THE WELL-KNOWN RIPOSTE TO THIS OFTEN-ASKED question is that it is a plant growing somewhere where it is not wanted. There are other qualities that can help to define a weed, though, and most gardeners who struggle to contain or, better, eliminate weeds from their plots will have a pretty good idea of what constitutes a weed in terms of sheer nuisance value.

FIGHTING THE BATTLE IN THE GARDEN

Home gardeners know that you should never leave a weed to set seed, or you will be increasing your problem a hundredfold. Even if you do not have time to weed thoroughly, make sure when you make a plot inspection that you pull off any buds or flowers you see on weeds – you can come back and attack the parent plant later.

An awe-inspiring but rather depressing statistic is that a hectare of land can contain as many as 555 million seeds in the top 15cm-layer of soil. And a lot of those seeds will not gladden your heart when they eventually germinate.

Born survivors

Weeds have a range of clever tricks to help them survive and thrive. They can grow quickly, and are often remarkably fertile, producing heroic quantities of seed. Some have seeds that can remain successfully dormant for long periods, germinating only when the conditions are just right and the resulting plants can take hold easily and vigorously.

▼ The roots of the dandelion, *Taraxacum officinale*, have dormant buds all along them (typically growing 40cm deep), so it can grow from any root fragment remaining in the soil.

Farmers prize clover, *Trifolium*, as a protein-rich forage for livestock that fixes its own nitrogen fertiliser, but it is less welcome in fine lawns.

Other weeds produce deep, inaccessible roots, or, smarter still, roots that have evolved to fragment when attempts are made to dig them up – meaning that every effort to get rid of them simply results in dozens of small, viable rooting pieces (known as 'ramets').

They also often mimic the life cycle or the specific qualities of the plants or crops that they infest. For example, lawn weeds, such as docks, *Rumex*, or clovers, *Trifolium*, tend to be low-growing so that they escape damage inflicted by the lawnmower, while blackgrass, *Alopecurus myosuroides*, a notorious weed in cereal crops, sets its seed just before the cereal is harvested, and then stays on to germinate in the autumn-sown crop.

Blackgrass, *Alopecurus myosuroides,* is an annual grass, found on cultivated and waste land. It is also known as slender meadow foxtail, twitch grass and black twitch.

A 'Weed' most often refers to a category of plants that are both highly adapted to grow successfully in gardens or within cultivated crops, and extremely difficult to get rid of. Weeds can spoil the effect that a gardener is aiming for in beds or borders, and in crop fields may reduce crop yield.

Why can grass be mown, but not other plants?

GRASSES HAVE LONG BEEN ACCUSTOMED to withstand the grazing habits of herbivores, from sheep to bison, and zebra to antelopes. And it is the resulting close-cropped, smooth appearance that has made it appealing to people and, over time, has developed the – very human – fetish for the perfect lawn. As every gardener knows, an immaculate lawn is hard to achieve, but the structure of grass plants does its best to help.

Growing from the ground up

The cells that divide to make plants grow are called the meristem. Plants that make appealing grazing, such as grass, would soon have died out if, as in many others, these cells were kept in the upper tip of the growing plant. Instead, they have evolved so that the meristem with its growing cells is placed at the base of the plant, the point where it grows from the soil. So grazing herbivores get their meal and the grass can continue to grow after they are cropped. Mowing performs the same job as grazing, leaving a neat, uniform mat of healthy plants.

The reason that grass plants can be mown without damaging them is that, unlike broader-leaved plants that grow from the top, they instead grow from the base, at soil level.

FINE TURF FOR ALL

Before the invention of lawnmowers, which made fine turf accessible to all, gardeners would either have to hire a flock of sheep to keep their lawns in check, or, when the grass was wet with dew, trim it back using a scythe, a slow and skilled job. While the first lawnmowers were human- or pony-powered, the very latest innovation in lawnmowing technology are robotic mowers. These noiseless devices can be set on a timer to trim grass within an area bounded by a buried wire automatically, without even the need for human supervision.

Why don't all the seeds I scatter grow?

IT IS A PIECE OF LONG-ESTABLISHED GARDENER'S LORE that you will get better results from seeds that you have gathered yourself, from growing plants, than you will from seeds bought in a packet. But is this true? And if so, why does home-gathered seed have an advantage?

Seed for sale is usually produced in countries with both dry climates and relatively cheap labour – for example, New Zealand and Kenya are major sources of garden seed. But the storage and transportation involved in getting the seed to markets far away inevitably takes time and may also subject it to fluctuations in humidity and temperature, which are not good for its growing prospects. When it reaches a seed merchant, the seed is graded, the top grade going to commercial growers, and the smaller seed, which usually carries less substantial food reserves, marketed more cheaply to domestic gardeners.

▲ Only pumpkin seeds from plants grown in isolation from other cultivars will produce plants similar to their parents, as pumpkins interbreed freely.

A Gathered seed has not usually had far to travel before being planted. In contrast, many seeds bought commercially will have come a long way and gone through numerous processes, all of which may impact on their vigour.

Having been through this, the packaged seed may then spend a considerable amount of time on the shelf in the shop – again, subject to fluctuations in temperature.

All these factors will count when it comes to setting home-gathered against commercially bought seed. You can give yourself a small advantage, though, by ensuring that any seed you buy comes from a seed merchant rather than a shop. It is more likely to be stored properly and sold promptly.

What seeds can be collected at home?

SINCE HOME-GATHERED SEEDS are generally more successful than those that are bought, most home gardeners, at some point in their gardening history, will have tried to collect and store the seeds from plants they like – both to grow for themselves and to share with others. There are various methods, depending on the type of plant that you are collecting from.

Any seeds can be collected at home: the key to successful collection and subsequent germination is to make sure that you collect the seeds at the right time and in the right way.

Harvesting: when and how

As a rule of thumb, the seed matures around two months after the plant flowers. It is best to look regularly at the plants you are planning to harvest from – get into the habit of checking them on your daily walk around the garden – and estimate when they are about to shed their seed for themselves, as this is the best time for you to collect. The home advantage is that you can collect here and there, as it suits individual plants, rather than going for a one-off collection as commercial growers have to, when some seeds may have already started to distribute themselves and others will not be quite ready.

When you think a plant is ready to seed, you can pick sprays or pods,

◀ Natural carrot seeds are impossibly hairy and bind to each other, but packet seeds have been 'milled', the fluff removed to make them easy to sow.

◀ Tomato and cucumber fruits are pulped and left to ferment. The seeds are then collected by passing the pulp through a sieve.

and either place them in a paper bag (especially suitable for the sort of podded seeds that 'explode' when they are mature) or in a tray lined with newspaper. When the sprays have dried, shake the seeds out, transfer them to small packets, label with the name of the plant and the date of collection, and store them in a cool, dry place until it is time to sow them.

Some seeds, such as those of tomatoes and cucumbers, need to be separated from the pulpy flesh of the fruit, and so call for a different method. Cut the fruits open, carefully scrape out the seedy pulp, mix it with a little water and leave it to ferment for a few days, after which the pulp can easily be washed off, and the seed separated out and left to dry on newspaper or kitchen towel before storing.

SEED SWAPS

Keen gardeners have always swapped home-grown seeds – for instance, one person's heirloom tomato seeds may be exchanged for someone else's heavy-cropping runner beans. Increasingly, though, seed-swapping events are becoming popular. Keep an eye out for 'Seedy Sunday' posters and advertisements in the local press, as these occasions offer a great chance not only to discover some new and interesting seed varieties but also to meet fellow gardeners and exchange growing news and information. If you want to partake yourself, make sure your seed is properly packaged in small envelopes and correctly labelled with its name and the date it was gathered, plus any information about growing and the qualities of the mature plant that you think another gardener will find useful.

How long can plants live?

IT DEPENDS ON WHAT YOU MEAN BY 'LIVE'. Some plants have effectively become immortal through repropagation – being endlessly renewed through their growing buds and shoots. Grapes, *Vitis*, that are still grown today are reputed to have ancient origins – 'Thompson Seedless' and 'Black Corinth' could both be as much as two thousand years old.

If you don't count repropagation, plants do have a measurable lifespan. Trees are the longest-lived true plants, but even they do not live for ever. Most trees die after about 500 years, although there are exceptions to this broad rule and many survive for considerably longer.

Plants are unlike animals in that they age unevenly. An animal ages uniformly – a tiger's tail is as old as its ears and its liver – but the growing tips of tree shoots and roots can remain young and active, often for centuries, when the main part of the plant is in decline. Trees are also able to compartmentalise damage, an asset that can enable them to survive some serious mishaps, including accidents and the ravages of pests and diseases.

Greek 'Black Corinth' grapes, *Vitis*, have been dried to make currants for 2,000 years or more. The ancient plants have effectively become immortal through repropagation.

THE OLDEST TREES IN THE WORLD

Really long-lived species of trees seem to have developed individual strategies which enable them to hang on. Coast redwoods, *Sequoia sempervirens*, for example, under the right circumstances, can grow staggeringly tall, enabling them to continue to service their living tissue for a couple of millennia, while yews, *Taxus*, can manage their own decline to a remarkable degree, hollowing out while becoming wider and wider at the base, and losing whole sections while regrowing others – some examples are believed to be as much as 5,000 years old. The Bristlecone pines, *Pinus longaeva*, that grow in the deserts of Nevada in the USA have used the harsh environment to their advantage, slowing their growth to a near standstill; one example, nicknamed Prometheus, which was felled in 1964, contained 4,900 growth rings.

Bristlecone pine,
Pinus longaeva

Even so, most trees die after about 500 years. Their sheer size is the undoing of them – eventually, they get so big and have such a vast area of living tissue to support that they cannot generate enough food to keep growing. And as they become low on nourishment, they begin to retrench, losing branches and becoming smaller and smaller until they run out of steam – they literally grow themselves to death.

Cheating their way to old age

There are a few honourable exceptions that have evolved ways around the too-large-to-live problem. Oak, *Quercus*, trees, for example, have a habit of dying back and then enjoying a resurgence – apparently moribund oaks, having lost their upper branches, will then pick themselves up and regrow lesser shoots once more from lower down on the tree. Usually, the upper shoots and branches of a tree, when in growth, release hormones that suppress the lower buds, but the oak appears to be able to reverse the process and begin to grow again before, as much as a century later, going into another cycle of retrenchment. In this way an oak can spin its life out far beyond most trees' natural span.

How fast can trees grow?

THE SPEED AT WHICH TREES GROW depends on a number of different factors, above and beyond whether or not the tree is by nature fast- or slow-growing. They include temperature, light levels, how much moisture is available, and whether or not a young tree has access to enough nutrients. If all these elements are present, some trees can put on growth surprisingly fast.

Live fast, die young

Young trees grow faster than old ones – if you look at a cross-section of the trunk of a large felled tree, you will see that the oldest rings nearer the centre of the trunk are generally much wider than those at the outer edge. Growth slows as the tree matures, and gets even slower as it nears the end of its natural lifespan: once the annual ring narrows to just 0.5mm or so, the tree is at death's door. Some trees, such as birches, *Betula*, tend to live fast and die young – few last beyond 80 years, which is young for a tree – and produce a wide growth ring every year until they collapse suddenly into old age and quickly perish.

Gardeners planting trees have to decide whether they want fast growth or something to leave to posterity: while a birch will easily mature and give pleasure as a tree within a lifetime, an oak, *Quercus*, is definitely an investment for coming generations.

Lone trees adopt a spreading habit, but in company with other trees they compete for light with their brethren and strive to become tall and narrow.

In the tropics, bamboo can grow as much as 50cm in a single day. British trees are not so hasty: they do not grow in winter and do not have the light and warmth to grow very fast even in summer, but, depending on species, most will add 15–50cm growth every year.

Do seeds have to be small to be spread by the wind?

WIND IS ONE OF THE MAIN FACTORS in seed distribution, and seeds have evolved in a number of ways to take advantage of natural breezes to spread themselves over as wide an area as possible. This usually involves incorporating some kind of a device in the outer casing of the seed to react helpfully when the winds blow.

Many airborne seeds are tiny; orchid seeds are microscopic, hardly bigger than a speck of dust. 1,000 willow seeds weigh just 0.05g. For comparison, 1,000 rice seeds weigh 27g. However, plants are skilled aerodynamicists. The seeds of sycamore, *Acer pseudoplatanus*, are relatively large (1,000 seeds weigh 97g), but their aerodynamic 'helicopter' shape means they can be carried far and wide in the right breeze. The largest airborne seeds are said to belong to the Javan cucumber, *Alsomitra macrocarpa*, a tropical plant that produces seeds with 15cm wings. Presumably, such large seeds are very 'expensive' to produce, which would explain why a relatively small number are made by the plant.

Plants that use airborne seeds tend to be opportunists: willows, *Salix*, (0.5g per 1,000) typically seed on land recently under water, while European ash, *Fraxinus excelsior*, (60–80g per 1,000) is the first to grow in spaces left by fallen trees.

Most airborne seeds are tiny. Some larger seeds are equipped with devices such as wings and parachutes, allowing them to be carried by the wind and travel further afield.

Shepherd's purse, *Capsella bursa-pastoris*, scatters up to 50,000 seeds to the breeze from its capsules. Sometimes, the whole stalk is blown away, scattering the seeds.

Why do shrubs seem to grow even faster after being pruned back?

THE KEY WORD HERE IS 'SEEM': if you measured its growth a year later, a shrub would be smaller if it had been pruned than it would have been if you had not pruned it. But shrubs can recover fast from even a heavy pruning, and the growth spurt that often seems to happen directly after can leave gardeners with the impression that pruning actually makes plants larger.

How the growth spurt works

The root/shoot balance is the mutual dependence between the roots (which are necessary to supply the shoots with water and nutrients) and the shoots (which feed the roots with sugar made by the process of photosynthesis in the plant's leaves). There must be healthy roots to feed the shoots, and vice versa. And if the shoots are pruned back, the roots will carry on feeding new growth to compensate.

The tips of branches in which a plant's cell division and growth happen are called the apices. One of their jobs is to send inhibiting hormones back down the branch to stop lower buds from shooting, so that growth is concentrated at the ends of the branches – in technical speak, they 'dominate' these lower buds. But when you prune a shrub, and cut the branch

▼ Apical dominance, the dominance of buds over others lower down the plant, defines the shape of how plants grow and how they respond to pruning.

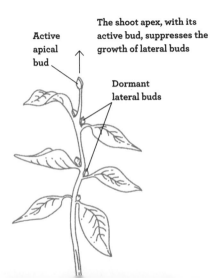

Active apical bud

The shoot apex, with its active bud, suppresses the growth of lateral buds

Dormant lateral buds

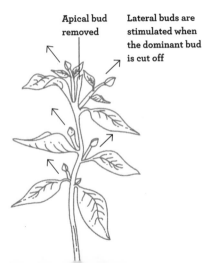

Apical bud removed

Lateral buds are stimulated when the dominant bud is cut off

ARapid growth in a shrub straight after it has been pruned is down to two factors: the plant's natural root/shoot balance and a more complicated phenomenon called apical dominance.

tips, the hormones are no longer sent back down to the lower buds. Thus, the inhibition is lifted, and there will be a sudden flush of several shoots emerging just below the pruning cut.

As the shrub eagerly reasserts its root/shoot balance and the apical dominance is released in favour of multiple shoots from each branch, an inexperienced gardener may well be asking themselves why they bothered to prune in the first place.

▲ Japanese spirea, *Spirea japonica*: one stem in three is removed completely after flowering to keep the bush compact and to induce new shoots that flower best.

PRUDENT PRUNING

Experienced pruners will spread a heavy pruning over several seasons, avoid drastic changes in shoot length, and thin the resulting 'water' shoots (those that rapidly spring up, often in a rather unattractive growth pattern, in response to pruning), leaving enough to sustain the plant's roots, but not so many that it regains its former size.

◀ Flowering currant, *Ribes sanguineum*, is an invaluable early flowerer. Removing one stem in three to near ground level after flowering counters their tendency to become 'stretched'.

How long can a seed remain alive?

EVERY SO OFTEN THERE WILL BE A NEWS REPORT that seeds recovered from an archaeological site have sprouted after being hidden away for centuries. While the evidence attached to these claims is sometimes questionable, it is certainly true that, although seeds start to deteriorate as soon as they are shed by the parent plant, the process is slow and can be made much slower by careful storage.

When stored in very dry and very cold conditions, seeds have been proven to survive for several centuries. In the hands of gardeners most garden seeds are much shorter-lived!

Slow burners

There are some confirmed record-breakers when it comes to the search for the world's oldest viable seed. Stored 'sacred' lotus, *Nelumbo*, seeds have been recovered from ancient sites several times and subsequently germinated, even at around a thousand years old (these seeds have also bucked the 'dry and cold' storage rule by being recovered from wet environments – but this makes sense, as the lotus is an aquatic plant). Date-palm, *Phoenix dactylifera*, seed is reported to have germinated after being stored for two millennia. The outright winner, though, is some catchfly, *Silene*, seed that Russian scientists claim to have germinated after a 32,000-year break. If their experiment can be repeated, the threshold of seed longevity will have been dramatically pushed back.

◀ For more than 5,000 years date palms, *Phoenix dactylifera*, have been grown where the climate is intensely hot and dry, but where groundwater is abundant, such as oases.

IN IT FOR THE LONG TERM: SEED BANKS

Seed or gene banks are collections of seeds whose survival in the
wild or under cultivation is threatened, but which may have a key
role in breeding food crops or maintaining biodiversity in the future.
Most banks rely on costly and potentially unreliable refrigeration, but
the Global Seed Vault, housed on the Arctic island of Spitsbergen, keeps
its seeds in near-ideal storage conditions in long tunnels bored into a
mountain of frozen rock. Currently, it stores more than 860,000 samples,
at a temperature of -18°C, and the scientists who run it expect these
seeds to last several centuries at least without degrading. In a more
everyday environment, here is how long you can expect your
own garden seeds to remain viable:

Up to three years:
Snapdragon, *Antirrhinum*, foxglove,
Digitalis, lettuce, leek and onion,
pansy, *Viola × wittrockiana*, parsley,
parsnip, sweetcorn.

Up to six years:
Broccoli, carrot, courgette, cucumber,
nasturtium, *Tropaeolum*, tobacco
plant, *Nicotiana*, wallflower, *Erysimum*,
zinnia, *Zinnia*.

Up to nine years:
Cabbage, swede, turnip

Common foxglove,
Digitalis purpurea

Up to ten years:
Radish, tomato

Radish,
Raphanus sativa

What would happen if the lawn wasn't mown for a year?

ONE OF THE MAIN FACTORS THAT KEEPS A LAWN lawnlike is regular mowing. What could you expect if you stopped mowing, not just for a week, but for months, or even years? The answer lies with the plants that make up your lawn in the first place.

Lawns are artificial communities, maintained by mowing and feeding to give the lawn grass – short and often 'creeping' in habit – an edge. As a lawn matures, however, weed grasses such as the atmospherically named Yorkshire fog, *Holcus lanatus*, will creep in and, if control stops, will literally make hay, and quickly dominate.

Given more time, as months changed to years, tree seedlings would grow. Birds would excrete pips and squirrels would bury acorns and nuts, while airborne seeds such as

Yorkshire fog,
Holcus lanatus

Turf grass is adapted to being grazed by sheep or other livestock. Modern lawns are 'grazed' by lawnmowers. When the grazing stops, the lawn grasses become vulnerable to competition from bigger grasses and taller, tougher weeds.

sycamore, *Acer pseudoplatanus*, and ash, *Fraxinus*, would arrive. Soon there would be the makings of a forest – the natural state of most British land. Within a decade or two, the short-lived trees, such as birch, *Betula*, and willow, *Salix*, would themselves give way to ash and oak, *Quercus*. Given long enough, the landscape would be completely wild, ready for the return of beavers.

When does a shrub become a tree?

THE SIMPLE ANSWER IS THAT TREES have a single main trunk, with branches well above ground level, and a mass of growth at the top. Shrubs, on the other hand, have a number of stems growing at or near ground level. But of course, there are exceptions to this basic rule.

Some trees, such as hazel, *Corylus*, are very large, but naturally send up multiple stems/branches from near-ground level, while some other genera, for example sweet chestnuts, *Castanea*, and various willows, *Salix*, are pruned every 10–15 years to generate many long, fast-growing stems. These are traditionally used as light timber in agriculture, building, charcoal burning, fencing and horticulture.

What about height? That is not a cut-and-dried factor, either. The professional view, from foresters and landscape gardeners, is that a plant more than 8m high is a tree, but to the domestic gardener a 'tree' might be a much shorter plant – anything more than 3m tall. Shrubs, on the other hand, may be as tall or wide or both as some of the smaller trees.

If you have a small garden, you can train plants that are technically shrubs to grow taller and to reduce the number of their stems, so that they can stand in for trees. Three shrubs that work well in this context are the smoke tree, *Cotinus coggygria*, the serviceberry *Amelanchier canadensis*, and Vilmorin's rowan, *Sorbus vilmorinii*.

▼ Shrubs are the toughies of the plant world, growing where trees fail. They spread risk by having several stems rather than just one trunk.

Shrubs lack a main trunk, having a number of stems that arise at or near ground level, while trees have a single main stem, branching well above ground level, and a mass of growth, or crown, at the summit.

Why are some carrots straight and others crooked?

IF YOU BUY YOUR CARROTS FROM A SUPERMARKET, you could be forgiven for thinking that all carrots are catwalk-ready – straight, evenly shaped and sometimes (if the supermarket is particularly high-end) presented with perfect topknots of bright green fronds attached. If you grow them yourself, however, you will know that the truth is quite different.

Sensitive vegetables

There is a long list of circumstances that can put carrot seeds out and cause them to fork or grow crooked. If they are transplanted from seed trays, they almost invariably fork, and if the soil they are growing in has compacted layers, or is stony or waterlogged, the carrot will grow crooked, and will fork or grow around obstacles, even small ones. Clumsiness or thinning out seedlings later than usual can also upset carrots and cause a crooked or misshapen harvest, as can over-enthusiastic hoeing and weeding.

Microscopic worms, engagingly called 'stubby-root nematodes' may also be the culprit if carrots are

◀ Orange carrots, introduced by the Dutch in the 15th century, replaced black, purple or white roots. Now 700,000 tonnes are grown annually in the UK.

A Carrot seedlings have very sensitive roots, are easily upset and are vulnerable to even small disturbances of the soil. They are also susceptible to predators, which can affect their root development.

grown in successive years in the same space – they only take hold when your crops are not regularly rotated, so, if they are possible culprits, move your carrot patch.

Crooked carrots have their place, however. Less-perfect specimens are used in cattle food, and, increasingly, sold in special packs of labelled 'wonky veg' at a reduced price in the shops, reflecting a general increasing awareness of food waste. While they are harder to peel, this is offset by their cheaper price – however many legs a carrot has, it is just as nutritious.

HOW TO GROW THE PERFECT CARROT

You can follow the lead of those specialists who grow the exhibits at horticultural shows. Here is how:

• Fill a tall cylinder, such as a 180-litre oil drum, with coarse sand.

• Use a crowbar to make conical holes in the sand – no more than six per drum – and fill them with a mix of equal parts of sieved, sterile soil and organic compost (specialists sometimes also add nutrients, which can be bought online or at your local nursery).

• Sow carrot seed in the holes.

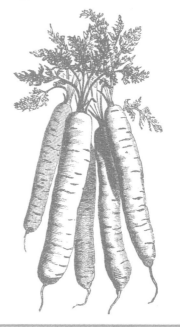

In the absence of any hindrances to the roots, and with the ideal conditions for growth, this process should result in evenly shaped carrots without forking.

Choose a short-rooted type to increase your chances of success – long-rooted varieties are the most likely to grow crooked. Tubby 'Chantenay' varieties are a good pick.

Q Why can't you buy orchid seeds?

ORCHID SEEDS ARE EXCEPTIONALLY TINY – they look just
like grains of dust. There are pros and cons to this minute scale
– unlike larger seeds, they carry hardly any food reserves, which
means that they risk starvation when they germinate, before they
are able to photosynthesise, but, on the plus side, they are so small
that the parent plant can produce them in huge numbers, so only a
teeny proportion needs to succeed.

Growing partners

In making seed that does not carry
food reserves, orchids have given
themselves a problem, but they have
evolved further to solve it themselves,
too. They have formed associations
with particular kinds of fungi that
will feed the germinating seed and
keep it going until the baby plants
reach the stage at which they can
photosynthesise and feed themselves.
As the relevant fungus cannot be
offered in packets alongside the seed,
and the seed will not survive without
it, orchid seed is not available on the
general market. Specialists, however,
buy something more rarefied: flasks,
containing both germinated seed
and an artificially created medium
inoculated with the relevant fungus.

◀ Tissue culture (micropropagation)
of orchids has reduced production
costs and, as a result, orchids are now
believed to be the top-selling UK
flowering house plant.

ANot only are they small, but orchid seeds are also difficult to germinate successfully. They are too complicated for the home gardener to be able to grow – which is why you will never see a packet of orchid seeds on sale.

You have to be dedicated to grow orchids this way – the process calls for repeated transfers to larger flasks as the baby plants grow, and it will be several years before the work results in mature plants that are capable of flowering. Micropropagation in specialised labs is another, speedier, solution to creating orchids in quantity.

Some amateurs try the natural route, reasoning that if orchid seed is scattered around the parent plant, the necessary fungus will be present already. It is a hit-and-miss system, but it sometimes works!

DO OTHER PLANTS PRODUCE SUCH TINY SEEDS?

Orchids are not the only group that relies on quantity over heft. The production of a lot of seeds in the hope that just a few will survive is quite common. Some of the most successful – and rapacious – examples are the witchweed, *Striga*, group, plants that originated in Asia but have spread to hot places all over the world. Being parasitic, they cause problems in many grass crops such as sorghum, millet and maize. Their success is due to the fact that each parent plant produces half a million seeds which, being small and light, spread widely, carried on the slightest breeze, and which can remain dormant but viable for up to a decade.

Witchweed,
Striga elegans

Where do cacti come from?

CACTI ARE THE TOUGH SURVIVALISTS of the plant world. They have evolved to cope in harsh, dry, desert surroundings, resulting in some unusual features, some obvious, some less so. Most of them have spines rather than leaves, large spherical or cylindrical bodies in which they can store water, and thick waxy skins to prevent evaporation.

We all think we know what a 'typical' cactus looks like, but there are a number of variations of both function and looks within the family. Wild desert cacti, such as the tall, branched saguaro, *Carnegiea gigantea*, from the Sonora Desert in the southwest USA, have extensive but shallow root systems to gather the rare rainfall as efficiently as possible. Other types have moved upward and dispensed with roots altogether, living in trees and relying on dew and rain for the occasional drink. Many open their stomata (plant pores) at night rather than during the day, to minimise the losses from evaporation, but still manage the crucial process of photosynthesis by a complex chemical process that allows them to delay carbon dioxide release until daytime, when there is sunlight for them to work with. Unsurprisingly, most cacti are very slow growers.

Old-fashioned Westerns all rely on a cactus-rich landscape to lend atmosphere, and the vast majority of the *Cactaceae* family do come from the Americas. Desert regions in other parts of the world have developed cactuslike plants – for example, the charmingly named African milk barrel, *Euphorbia horrida*, a native of South Africa – but they are not members of the same family.

Why do some people talk to plants?

DEPENDING ON YOUR PREFERRED MEDIA SOURCE, people who talk to plants are either deranged or visionary. Less clear is whether or not the plants enjoy the conversation. 'Plant whisperer' stories in the media are common, but do not usually have any hard scientific study to back them up.

The principle behind the idea that talking to plants is good for them is that the person talking is breathing out carbon dioxide, which benefits the plant. This does not bear up under examination – the CO_2 in human breath dissipates very quickly, too fast for the plant to enjoy any benefit.

On the same level are the claims that different types of music have a beneficial effect on plants: an easy press filler, but without supporting evidence. However, it would be unwise to dismiss chatting to your plants out of hand: artificially raising CO_2 levels in a greenhouse on a sunny day has been shown to give a substantial boost to plant growth. It would, though, take a seriously prolonged monologue in a very well-lit, sheltered spot to raise CO_2 to the level at which it might have a significant effect.

And is it good for you to talk to your plants? This is less controversial: there are numerous studies showing that growing plants and caring for them is psychologically beneficial, reducing stress and countering depression.

Touch, don't talk

If talking to plants does not seem to be getting you results, try touching them gently instead. You will be mimicking the effects of a light wind, and plants respond to breezes by growing sturdier, with thicker stems and denser foliage.

What is an alien invader?

IF A WEED IS A PLANT IN A PLACE where it does not belong, an alien invader is the supercharged version. These aren't the intergalactic kind of visitors, but they can wreak surprising amounts of havoc in new territories and they can take over completely in places that unwittingly prove hospitable to them, sometimes at an astonishing rate.

Unwanted visitors

The classic example of an alien invader is Japanese knotweed, *Fallopia japonica*. In its native Japan, knotweed is meek and unassuming, probably because it evolved alongside the predators and diseases that kept it under control. When it moved abroad, though, its personality changed. An attractive plant, it was introduced to Britain by the Victorians, although by 1907 it was already mentioned in gardening guides as being 'easier to plant than to get rid of'. Today, it is notorious as one of the most pernicious weeds known in the UK. On farmland, grazing animals and regular ploughing prevent it from becoming a problem, but it is perfectly

An alien invader is a plant from another part of the world that is introduced, either deliberately or by accident, into a new region. Without the diseases and predators that keep them in check at home, invaders can sometimes run amok.

Japanese knotweed, *Fallopia japonica*, plants in Britain are all female. If male plants arrive, seed production will be possible, and, with that variation, make control even more difficult.

THE WORLD'S WORST WEED

In 2014, the International Union for the Conservation of Nature organised a poll to establish the worst weed in the world. From a line-up of horrors, the dubious honour was eventually awarded to Kariba weed, *Salvinia molesta*, an aquatic fern that originated in Brazil. In many countries it has thrived wherever it has been introduced, clogging canals and rivers and creating problems in reservoirs and hydroelectric facilities. Its rampant growth smothers other aquatic life, while its rotting remains take oxygen from the water, threatening populations of fish and other water animals.

The common rhododendron, *Rhododendron ponticum*, is highly invasive in the UK and parts of France. It produces up to a million seeds each year, dispersed by the wind for up to 500m.

adapted to urban life and rapidly develops immensely deep and resilient root masses that are resistant to anything other than the most laborious extraction (which usually calls for a mechanical digger) or the most intensive application of weedkillers for at least two years. It can regrow from the tiniest part of a residual root, and thrives particularly on riverbanks and canals. Without any natural curbs, fighting its spread is a losing battle.

The real danger of alien invaders is the threat they pose to biodiversity. As with Japanese knotweed, many were originally imported as decorative novelties, so they often look appealing, but they behave like thugs, smothering less assertive plants. Other examples that have taken over in the UK include the common rhododendron, *Rhododendron ponticum*, originally from coastal regions of the Black Sea, which thrives on acid soils, forming huge woodland thickets that smother everything growing at a lower level, and the butterfly bush, *Buddleja*, which is popular with insects but which forces out many other plants.

What is the difference between a mushroom and a toadstool?

IN COMMON USAGE, WE CALL EDIBLE FUNGI MUSHROOMS, and inedible or poisonous ones toadstools. Is there a real distinction between the two? No: even if, in your mind's eye, a mushroom is something deliciously sizzling in a pan, and a toadstool is a brilliant shade of red, with dangerous-looking, white spots – something you would not dream of eating – this isn't a scientific division.

The basidiomycota group covers a wide range of fungi, from puffballs, *Lycoperdon*, to honey fungus, *Armillaria mellea*. The latter, the bane of tree-loving gardeners, feeds on tree roots, forming a mat of fungal strands – mycelium – that also spreads up under the bark of the tree. The fungus gradually creates rhizomorphs, thicker, black, bootlace-like structures, that wind around the tree's roots, ultimately rotting them. As the tree sickens and dies, the rhizomorphs reach out to infect other trees nearby.

A mycologist, or fungi fancier, does not distinguish between toadstools and mushrooms: to them, both are simply the fruiting bodies of the group basidiomycota.

While the majority of infection by honey fungus is local, the mat of mycelium underground may sometimes also send up honey-coloured toadstools. These produce air-carried spores which can potentially spread the disease over wider distances.

Mushrooms to try

While there is no clear difference between a mushroom and a toadstool in scientific terms, it is important to know which mushrooms you can eat and which will make you sick when it comes to using them in the kitchen. Despite their murky reputation, very few fungi are poisonous enough to

◀ Honey fungus, *Armillaria mellea*, is one of the very few fungi that can kill living roots. Most toadstools are harmless.

THE BEST TO EAT

Beyond the everyday cultivated mushroom, *Agaricus bisporus*, other types that have become increasingly easy to buy are shiitake mushrooms, *Lentinus edodes*, tree oyster mushrooms, *Pleurotus ostreatus*, and, more rarely, lion's mane, *Hericium erinaceus,* and Indian oyster mushrooms, *Pleurotus pulmonarius*. Others that you are more likely to find at a farmer's market than in the store are the rich, meaty-tasting

Cultivated mushroom
Agaricus bisporus

horse mushrooms, *Agaricus arvensis*, and bright orange chanterelles, *Cantharellus cibarius*, which have a delicate, almost floral smell and flavour.

Truffles, those ultimate fungal luxuries, belong to a separate group: they are ascomycetes, rather than basidiomycetes.

Tree oyster mushroom,
Pleurotus ostreatus

make you really ill – only around 1 per cent could actually kill you – and in countries where there is an enthusiastic mushroom-gathering tradition, Italy and Georgia among them, the start of the mushroom season is greeted with excitement: amateur enthusiasts are very knowledgeable about what they can eat and what is best left alone. It is crucial to know what you are doing if you want to follow in their footsteps, but the range of cultivated mushrooms available grows ever wider, and farmer's markets are often happy hunting grounds for the foraged variety.

Why do some trees have needles?

As a general rule, the harsher the environment a plant grows in, the smaller its leaves. Needles carry leaf compaction to an extreme: each has a central vein surrounded by cells containing chlorophyll, and is waterproofed with a thick skin and waxy cuticle that reduce losses by evaporation. Pores, or stomata, are relatively few compared with the number on an ordinary leaf.

Needles are excellent at minimising water loss from a plant, so they work for plants from hot climates. They are also practical for trees from very cold climates where the ground is often frozen, making the take-up of water difficult.

Water conservation is not the only advantage that needles offer. Although needles are good at minimising water loss, each needle does not actually contain that much water. Therefore, if the water freezes, the subsequent damage is minimised. Furthermore, in blizzard conditions, heavy snowfall slides off the needles, and they also filter gales so that the tree's branches do not break.

Although most needle-bearing trees are evergreens, some, the European larch, *Larix decidua*, for example, are deciduous, shedding their needles in autumn. These tend to be the trees that live in the harshest conditions, so the shed helps them to get through the tough mountain winters.

SCALES VS NEEDLES

Some conifers, like Leyland cypress, *Cuprocyparis leylandii*, and the Western red cedar, *Thuja plicata*, have developed scales as an alternative to needles: scales, too, are compacted leaves that equip the plant for inhospitable conditions. A side effect is the trees' even appearance, making these species popular for dense hedging.

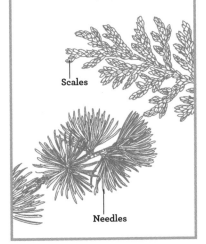

Scales

Needles

Why do some plants have thorns?

PLANTS ARE GOOD FOOD FOR MANY ANIMALS, and so they invest a lot of their resources into defending themselves. They lace themselves with toxic chemicals, they lay down harsh, abrasive tissue, coat themselves with tough hairs or waxy skins, and so on. And one of the commonest forms of plant defence is a liberal scattering of sharp thorns to see off animals whose mouths, skin and eyes are vulnerable to these home-grown daggers.

Common holly,
Ilex aquifolium

Spiky strategies

The common holly, *Ilex aquifolium*, offers a clever example of resource balancing. Its young leaves are leathery, waxy and formidably spiky,

Thorns are an important defence mechanism for some plants, but they are just one part of an overall strategy that engages some of the plant's energy stores in defence and the rest in the cycle of reproduction, ensuring the survival of the individual plant and the species.

and make a potent protection for the seedling. However, as the plant grows tall and reaches above the grazing height of animal predators, the leaves that the plant grows lose their spikes and become spineless, saving the holly's resources and becoming more effective at photosynthesis. The African gum arabic tree, *Acacia senegal*, has a similar strategy, losing its thorns as it gains in height, with the additional deterrent that it exudes a sticky gum, also believed to limit grazing.

What does the 'F$_1$' on seed packets mean?

MOST OF THE SEEDS YOU BUY to grow in a garden are hybrids – created by cross-breeding two genetically distinct but closely related parent plants. Although hybrids can occur naturally, by accidental cross-fertilisation, many new plants are created deliberately by plant breeders, who cross-breed, then select from the resulting progeny to get the best of different plants' characteristics combined into a new variety.

Hybrid benefits

The key to an F$_1$ hybrid lies in the inbred lines of its parent plants. Inbreeding means that the breeding has been strictly controlled, and both 'parents' have been self-pollinated. In 'outbreeding' the parent plants have been pollinated by other plants. Although maintaining the desirable characteristics that the plant breeders are looking for, inbreeding in plants, as with animals, is also associated with a loss of health and vigour and a reduction in genetic variability – the shallower the gene pool that any organism is paddling in, the less vital it is likely to be.

AN EXPENSIVE ENTERPRISE

It is technically complex and very costly to develop and maintain inbred parent lines that combine well and result in the ideal offspring that have all the desirable traits of their parents. But the plants bred are often valuable enough to repay the effort and, in saving and marketing their own seeds, commercial growers can avoid piracy of the key genetic mixes. If a pair of F$_1$ plants cross-pollinate in your garden, they will produce F$_2$ seedlings that are less constrained genetically, and will lack the 'heterosis' or hybrid vigour that occurs when inbred parents are crossed. They will therefore be more diverse and less vigorous – not the predictable, uniform result desired by most gardeners. To benefit from the predictable properties of F$_1$ hybrids, therefore, you have to buy fresh seed every year.

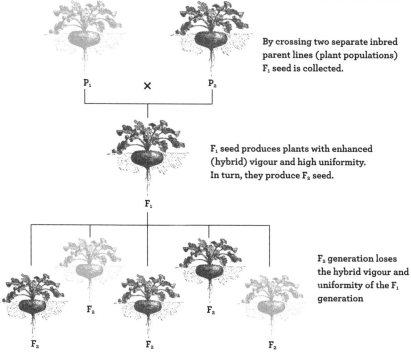

By crossing two separate inbred parent lines (plant populations) F_1 seed is collected.

F_1 seed produces plants with enhanced (hybrid) vigour and high uniformity. In turn, they produce F_2 seed.

F_2 generation loses the hybrid vigour and uniformity of the F_1 generation

However, if plants are repeatedly inbred until they have the same pairs of chromosomes (known as homozygous), and then bred again, a new strength emerges in their offspring, called hybrid vigour, or heterosis – and the end result is the production of identical plants that are also strong. This method is used commercially to create the large numbers of identical units that are desirable for crop growing or vast swathes of bedding plants, for example.

▼ Kohlrabi, like many cabbage family plants, cannot self-pollinate, but, if the unopened flowers are dissected and pollinated by hand, inbred plants can be produced.

A When 'F_1' appears on a packet of seeds, it means that the seeds inside are the first generation of a cross breeding – 'F' stands for 'filial', and the '1' denotes the generation the seeds come from.

Why do wild plants seem to thrive, when those carefully planted in the garden often die?

THIS IS A COMMON PERCEPTION, but it is not really right – in truth, a very low proportion of wild plant seeds survives to adulthood. The misconception usually arises because wild plant seeds that fall to the ground in any kind of artificial environment, whether it is a motorway embankment or a fertile garden, will find themselves without the usual levels of competition and will grow with unnatural ease and vigour.

The odds in the wild

To survive, wild plants must cast enormous numbers of seeds into the world in the hope of a few making it into adulthood and themselves reproducing. To take just one example: an oak, *Quercus*, tree will produce as many as 5 million acorns during its life – but they certainly will not result in more than a few trees, even if it is lucky in its situation. Roughly 90 to 100 per cent of all seeds are eaten or die before they even have the chance

It is easier to see the failures among the plants you have chosen and planted yourself, and these may occur for all kinds of reasons. What you do not see are the vast numbers of wild plants that never make it to maturity.

▶ Oaks, *Quercus*, shed up to a tonne of acorns per tree. Just 18 trees per hectare could out yield wheat (the UK wheat record is currently 16 tonnes per hectare).

THE MAIN REASONS CULTIVATED PLANTS FAIL

Sometimes, gardeners have themselves to blame, but there are some innate characteristics of garden plants and seeds that can lead to disappointment.

- **Poor seed.** Commercial seeds cannot be fresh: they have to be gathered, cleaned, packed and marketed. And the seed quality can fail during the time this takes.

- **Weather.** Every plant, everywhere, can fall victim to bad weather. An out-of-season frost or a prolonged drought can see off otherwise healthy plants.

- **Over-protected root systems.** When you buy a plant in a nursery, it will usually have been grown in a specialist potting medium in the unnatural environment of a pot that is frequently watered and probably also treated with fertiliser and pesticides. When transplanted into garden soil, which may be heavy, wet, cold, slow-draining or all of the above, the plant's mollycoddled root system will be unable to cope.

to germinate. The lucky few that arrive on a patch of ground free from annihilating competition and are able to germinate will largely either be eaten or will succumb to competition from stronger plants. Going back to that oak, the few seedlings that have resulted from those acorns will have to survive weather, pests and diseases, as well as the possibility of being snacked on by herbivores, for a full 20 years before they can breed themselves. If farmers or gardeners faced the same odds as are set up for wild plants, most would admit defeat.

Add some cultivation and husbandry, though, and the plants immediately achieve much greater success. Orchard trees, planted in considered conditions, are expected to achieve a 95 per cent success rate. Of a packet of commercial carrot seed, around 80 per cent of the seeds should germinate, and around 50 per cent will make it to viable seedlings.

Is the air inside a bell pepper the same as the air outside?

THIS RATHER SPECIALIST QUESTION is a perennial favourite, and a number of experiments have been conducted to get at the truth. The smooth, apparently poreless outer skin of a bell pepper, *Capsicum annuum,* leads to the supposition that the pepper cannot 'breathe' and, therefore, that the air inside must have its own atmosphere.

Despite the shiny exterior, there is probably some limited diffusion between the inside and outside of the pepper – or the interior atmosphere would have an even higher level of carbon dioxide. One experiment into seed development in peppers artificially reduced the amount of oxygen inside the fruit – and this was found to affect the seeds adversely.

The conclusion was that the peppers have enough control over their inner microclimate to allow successful seed development.

As ever, answering one question raises others: does the air in peppers vary at day and night times? Does the air change as a pepper grows? And so on. Useful or not, internet speculation can continue for a while yet.

Tests conclude that the air outside and the pepper's internal air are actually different. Regular air contains roughly 78 per cent nitrogen and 21 per cent oxygen, with traces of argon, carbon dioxide, water vapour and other gases; 'pepper' air has 2–3 per cent less oxygen and up to 3 per cent more carbon dioxide.

How do seeds know which way is up?

SEEDS DO NOT USUALLY get it wrong when they germinate; whichever way the seed is placed in the ground, the emerging root seems to head to the soil and the shoot starts growing towards the light. But how do seeds know which way they should grow? Do they ever make mistakes?

The only way is up – or down

Roots need to grow down, as without secure anchorage and access to water, the seedling is unlikely to survive. In fact, plant roots show a marked inclination to grow downwards – the technical term is gravitropism – and although little is known about the mechanism that decides this, it is believed to operate through statocytes (cells that may be able to sense gravity) which are located in the root tip. If the tip is destroyed, the root will not grow downwards until it is repaired. The same principle is thought to be in play when side roots grow outwards, except that in this case the statocytes promote lateral rather than vertical growth.

Shoots also have statocytes arranged all along them. The cells are rich in starch, and the starch settles down under gravity and promotes upward growth. Because each shoot has these gravity-sensing cells all along it, rather than just in the tip, upward growth continues even if the shoot is damaged.

▶ In hypogeal germination, as shown here, the seed remains below ground. In epigeal germination, the root grows down while the seed is lifted by the extending shoot.

Seeds are dormant until germination; they have no way of sensing their orientation. Once they germinate, however, the new roots and shoots are finely attuned to gravity and head reliably up or down.

How fast does water travel in a plant?

IN ORDER TO PHOTOSYNTHESISE, plants need plenty of water. The process of transpiration means that the plant 'swaps' water for the carbon dioxide that is a key part of its food-making process – the water is expelled from the plant's leaves as the carbon dioxide is taken in. But for transpiration to take place, the water needs to travel from the roots of the plant up to its leaves.

TRANSPIRATION IN ACTION

There is an experiment you can do to watch transpiration in action. All you need is some red or blue food colouring and a few white carnations, *Dianthus*.

• Cut the ends of the carnation stems at 45 degrees, taking care not to crush them (or you will damage their internal mechanisms).

• Add some food colouring to a container of water, and place the carnations in it.

• Time how long it takes for the flowers to change colour. When they do, you can use the length of the stalk and the time it has taken for the water to travel up to the flower to work out the water's rate of travel.

▶ The stem of the central flower has been split lengthways and each half placed in a different colour dye, producing a flower with two distinct colours.

From root to branch

To some extent, the rate of travel depends on the rate at which water is taken up by a plant's roots. At its top level of transpiration, though, the quantity of water expelled by a tree through its leaves is quite impressive: on a hot, summer day, with a slight breeze, a large tree might shed as many as 2,000 litres every day, with peak loss occurring between midday and the point when the sun starts to dip in the late afternoon.

There are two ways of measuring the speed that water travels in the xylem (the circulatory vessels that connect roots to leaves in plants). The first is to add a dye to the water the roots take up and measure how long it takes to reach the leaves (see left). The second is to send a pulse of slightly warmer water up from the roots and measure how long it takes to travel a set distance up the stem or trunk.

This is not a huge challenge for a daisy, *Bellis perennis* – but in a forest tree water for transpiration must be lifted in substantial quantities and to quite a height. Studies show the rate varies. As you would expect, small amounts of water travel faster, larger quantities at a slower pace.

In experiments, it was found that rates varied significantly but, typically, water took just under half an hour to travel from the roots to the top of a 23m oak, *Quercus*, tree. In metres per hour, water travelled 43.6m in an oak tree, 25.7m in a common ash, *Fraxinus excelsior*, and at a substantially slower rate in a conifer – just 0.5m in an hour.

▶ Even if trees are of equal size, ash, *Fraxinus* (left), a vigorous, greedy pioneer species, can transfer water more quickly to its foliage than a conifer (right).

Can seeds be spread by water?

CERTAIN SEEDS ARE ESPECIALLY ADAPTED to water spread, although it is not always their primary means of dispersal, while others are accidentally washed to new land. Light, buoyant seeds that float naturally fare best in the water and can be carried great distances, washing up and subsequently germinating far away from their parent plant.

Water cruising

Seeds that travel by water do not risk dehydration, but also do not have much control over where they end up. Many streamside plants have light seeds that float readily and are mostly limited to wetlands – water hemlock, *Cicuta*, and the noxious and invasive giant hogweed, *Heracleum mantegazzianum*, both belong to the carrot family (which generally has light, corky seeds) and fetch up in large, often isolated strands when they find a favourable spot to germinate and grow. The poisonous Jimson weed, *Datura stramonium*, and many members of the sedge family,

Water hemlock, *Cicuta*, seeds float along ditches and rivers. Plants that arise can pose a threat to livestock grazing in meadows unless excluded by fencing.

Water is a good medium for seed spread – and plants use it, whether deliberately or not, more than you might expect. Streams, rivers, floodwaters and even the sea are all pressed into service when it comes to plants expanding their territory and colonising new lands.

Cyperaceae, also spread along riverbanks. Successful weeds do not always depend on one means of spread: docks, *Rumex*, for example, have winged seeds that are well adapted to both wind dispersal and water spread: the light wings lend seeds buoyancy in the water.

Accidental passengers

Irrigation systems are also a common means for seeds to spread. A survey in the United States found viable seeds of no fewer than 138 different weed species in irrigation water taken from the Columbia River, highlighting the opportunistic character of plants. As herbicide-resistant weeds become more common, the custom of filtering irrigation water may need to increase, to stop this way of spreading some very invasive species.

▲ Sea beans, seeds of riverside tropical leguminous trees in Central and South America, often wash up on British shores after a journey across the Atlantic.

SEAFARING COCONUTS

A surprising number of nuts and seeds are dispersed to new lands on ocean currents. Coconuts are some of the most impressive sailors: there are records of nuts floating from Melanesia to the eastern shores of Australia, and hearsay evidence of even longer voyages. It is not possible to be definitive about which populations in the world floated to their end destinations, and which had ancestors that were brought along on human sea voyages, but there is no arguing that, with its seed safely contained in a thick layer of endosperm (the white, meaty part of the coconut that we eat), then encased in a hard, woody 'nut' and, finally, with a wrapping of buoyant, fibrous husk, the coconut is ideally equipped for a lengthy sea journey.

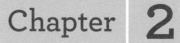

Chapter 2

Flowers and Fruits

Why don't fig trees have flowers?

THE CHINESE CALL THE FIG *wú huā guǒ*, literally 'the fruit with no flower'. Appearances are deceptive, however. Although they are not visible on the tree, figs do have flowers, or, to be more accurate, they have a flower-bearing organ, called the synconium. And the way that they fertilise and reproduce is very elaborate indeed.

Figs are unusual. The structure that we call the fig fruit is not technically a fruit at all: it is the synconium and is a swelling that is an extension of a stem of the tree. Each synconium forms a hollow chamber, lined with tiny individual flowers.

The perfect partnership

Fig trees can be either female or hermaphrodite, the latter having male and female flowers stored in separate synconia. Figs cannot ripen until they have been pollinated and this is managed with the attentions of a very tiny and very specialised wasp, *Blastophaga psenes*, under 2mm long.

The wasp's life cycle is intimately bound up with the fig and the two are mutually dependent on one another for their survival. Each synconium has a tiny natural opening, the ostiole, through which a female wasp squeezes. Although it is so small that she may lose her wings and antennae as she works her way in, this does not affect her ability to pollinate the flowers inside with pollen that she has carried with her from her parent fig, the one in which she was born.

The fig fruit, or syconium, produced by a pollinated female plant, is sweet and succulent.

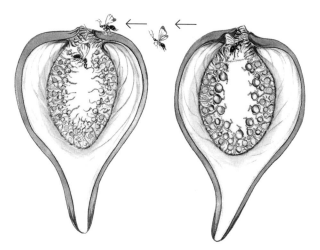

The *Blastophaga psenes* wasp develops in the male syconium of a hermaphrodite plant, then carries pollen to the flowers of the female plants.

Once pollination has taken place and the female wasp has laid her eggs, she dies. When her eggs hatch, the larvae will develop into pupae, and then emerge as mature wasps. The males will mate with the females, then tunnel out of the now-ripening fig. The females emerge through the tunnel and fly off to start the cycle all over again, while the ripened figs are eaten and have their seeds dispersed by animals.

The female flowers of the hermaphrodite plant are not pollinated, but do produce a seedless fruit. It does not become a sweet, succulent fig, and you would not want to eat it yourself, but goats seem happy enough to incorporate the small, hard fruits into their everyday diet.

There are some other examples of close and very specialised relationships between plants and their pollinators: the Cardinal flower, *Lobelia cardinalis*, for example, has elongated red flowers that can only be

VIRGIN FRUIT

Blastophaga psenes wasps live only in warm climates, but in colder countries parthenocarpic figs, which do not need fertilising to produce ripe fruit, have been developed by growers. The crop they produce is not usually of quite such high quality as the fertilised figs – you might not want to put it in your figgy pudding – but it is useful when the wasp is not available to do her very specialised work.

pollinated by hummingbirds, while the moth orchid, the type widely sold as a house plant, has mothlike flowers that flutter in the breeze, attracting moths that will transfer pollen from bloom to bloom.

Do apples really fall close to the tree?

AS THE OLD SAYING GOES, apples do fall close to the tree – gravity ensures that. However, the tree has produced a delicious fruit as part of its strategy to get its seeds taken some distance away – far enough to ensure that they will grow successfully and will not compete with the parent tree for sunlight and nutrients.

Not only will an animal transport the apple seed to a new spot to grow, but travelling on its own journey through that animal's digestive tract will also help to prepare the seed for rapid germination when it gets there.

Large, sweet, juicy fruits are hugely expensive for a tree to produce. The investment the parent makes is calculated, however: if the apples appeal to passing animals and are eaten, the seeds will then be excreted well away from the original tree.

Like father, like son?

Despite the trouble the tree has gone to, it might not recognise its offspring when they grow. Apple trees grown from seed seldom resemble their parents (or 'come true' in horticultural jargon), as apples' genetic make-up is very variable. Apples are also notoriously difficult to root as cuttings. So when breeders

Malus domestica 'Cox's Orange Pippin'. Braeburn, Cox, Gala and Bramleys dominate UK apple production. Delicious is the most popular EU apple.

Malus 'Hyslop'. This large crab apple of unknown origin was first recorded in 1869. It has dark red skin with purple overtones and its name is sometimes spelled Hislop.

want an apple tree that will reliably produce a specific fruit, they propagate their stock by grafting. This means that a budding piece of the desirable parent tree is inserted into a split in a young tree of the same or similar species (called the rootstock) so that the vascular, growing tissue of the two exactly line up. In time, the graft will 'take', producing a tree that will crop faithfully to the original parent.

ANY APPLE IS BETTER THAN NO APPLE

North America is especially rich in old and heirloom apple cultivars. This is partly said to be because the first pioneers travelling west had difficulty transporting living trees into the trackless interior by the slow and uncertain transport available to them. This left them with no choice but to establish their new orchards from apple seeds, which, while unreliable, were at least easy to carry. The resulting trees would have been highly variable and probably of relatively poor quality, but, in early pioneering days, any apple was better than no apple. And the widespread use of apple seed from all kinds of stock resulted in a large, diverse population of trees from which a few outstanding examples were subsequently propagated by grafting, and used for breeding.

Why are there so many different sorts of flower?

UNLIKE ANIMALS, PLANTS ARE STATIC, so they cannot seek out a mate, but they need help to reproduce – and this is the secret behind their diversity. The various solutions they find also make them extraordinarily important to other systems, both micro and macro: their role goes far beyond ensuring their own survival.

Pollination is the part of the cycle with which plants need help. Each flower structure either has to entice a pollen carrier – usually a bee or other insect, but more rarely a bird, or even a bat – to visit it, or it must be designed to make use of air currents to spread its pollen about.

Flowers need to gain an advantage over their rivals. They have evolved to do this in all kinds of ways: they may be attention-seeking in structure, colour or scent; or they may offer easy

A flowering plant needs not only to flower, but also to be pollinated and set seed to reproduce, and plants have arrived at all kinds of different ways to achieve this.

access to the nectar that insects are looking for. Many have developed to appeal to specific insects or groups: bell-shaped flowers, for example, are ideal for long-tongued, round-bodied bees, which can climb right inside the flower and use their tongues to reach nectar at the flower's base, while some highly evolved bee orchids, *Ophrys apifera*, actually take the form of the insect that they need to pollinate them.

DO-IT-YOURSELF FERTILISATION

Three quarters of all flowering plants combine male and female parts in the same flower. Although self-pollination is rarely ideal – cross-pollination, and plenty of it, leads to strong stock. It is something that plants can fall back on if all else fails.

Bee orchid,
Ophrys apifera

What is a double flower?

DOUBLE FLOWERS ARE EASILY recognised: they appear to be all petal, and so look more rounded and 'fluffier' than single flowers. By contrast, single flowers usually have a visible centre, made up of the stamens and carpel, respectively the male and female reproductive parts of the flower.

Dahlia, *Dahlia hortensis*

A double flower has an extra layer of petals that makes them striking to look at. Most double flowers have sacrificed their stamens and carpal for extra petals.

Double flowers arise by spontaneous mutation, and, lacking the reproductive parts of their single siblings, they are sterile: without either nectar or pollen, there is nothing to tempt insects to visit them. Even if the insects did visit, there would be no pollen for them to take to pollinate another flower. So double flowers can usually reproduce only by artificial means – cuttings, division or micropropagation. Despite this natural disadvantage, they are in high demand because of their showy appearance, so alert gardeners will spot them and grow them on as new cultivars.

MIXED DOUBLES

There are some exceptions to the sterility rule: double flowers in which the extra petals have not been added at the expense of the plant's reproductive system. In these, petals have replaced other parts of the flower, such as the bracts. In the case of double sunflowers, *Helianthus*, for example, the flower has literally been reorganised, with extra outer petals replacing the inner disc florets that would otherwise make up the centre.

Is there a way to check if a flower is male or female?

THE VAST MAJORITY OF FLOWERS ARE HERMAPHRODITE, having both male and female organs – the botanical term for this is 'perfect'. The male elements of a flower are the stamens and the pollen on them, while the female parts are the carpels, each of which holds an ovary at its base. The gametes, or sex cells of the plant, reside inside the pollen grains and the ovaries respectively.

Most flowers are hermaphrodite, having male and female organs. Just a little knowledge of flower anatomy makes it easy to identify their reproductive organs, even if the tiny scale of some flowers will call for the use of a magnifying glass.

The centre of the flower is occupied by the ovary, which contains the precursor to seeds (ovules). It bears the sticky stigma that collects pollen.

A naming of parts

The outer sections of a flower – the sepals and the petals – are not gender related. Move further into the bloom and you will find the stamens – threadlike structures that each support a head, or anther, inside which the pollen grains are produced. Collectively, the stamens are called the androecium, and they are often organised in distinctive patterns. The arrangements can be elaborate and complex, and can be helpful

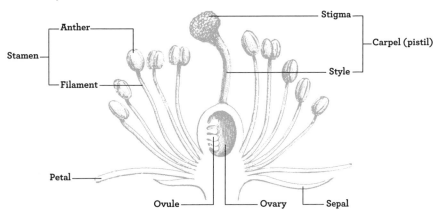

Stigma

Carpel (pistil)

Anther

Stamen

Style

Filament

Petal

Ovule

Ovary

Sepal

SINGLE-SEX PLANTS

Although most plants share both male and female parts in the same flower, there are plenty of exceptions. Some, such as hazel, *Corylus*, have separate flowers for their male and female organs on the same plant, while others have single-sex plants that need to encounter an example of the opposite sex to reproduce by fertilisation (the botanical term for this is 'dioecious'). One of these is the notorious Japanese knotweed, *Fallopia japonica*. In the UK, only female plants have ever been imported. Despite the fact that they do not have males to reproduce with, the females have achieved a rapid and invasive colonisation of their new territory simply by spreading and dividing their rhizomes: a staggeringly successful example of invasion against the odds.

Male flowers

Female flowers

Hazel,
Corylus avellana

when botanists are trying to identify an unfamiliar flower – androecium patterning is one of the characteristics that related plants often share.

Usually, the carpels are placed near the centre of the flower. Sometimes, they are laid out as individual units, but they may also be fused into a single structure or structures (flowers may have one or several), called the pistil. The collective name for the grouped female parts is the gynoecium, the female equivalent of the androecium. Although plenty

of different arrangements exist in different flowers, the simplest you will see – think of a buttercup, *Ranunculus*, for example – is the pistil or pistils in the centre, surrounded by a ring of stamens.

Buttercup,
Ranunculus

What does a bee see when it looks at a flower?

WHICH CAME FIRST, THE FLOWER OR THE BEE? Scientific research suggests that early bees existed before flowers – or at least, what we think of as flowers in the modern sense – so it is likely that the flower developed to please the bee, rather than the other way around.

Flowers that developed early in history, the magnolia, for example, seem to have made themselves attractive to as many potential pollinators as possible. Over time, however, evolutionary tactics changed: plants evolved to appeal to specific insect pollinators. Those that were best pollinated by bees needed to find ways of showing off to a bee's way of seeing. And although bees see ultraviolet light, their large, compound eyes are not very precise – they cannot make out the different parts of a flower as easily as we can.

BIRD, BEE OR BUTTERFLY?

Every pollinator has its preferred range in the colour spectrum. Flowers that have evolved to be pollinated by bees tend towards the blue-to-violet range (particularly those that also gleam in ultraviolet light, invisible to us). Birds, though, favour red and orange flowers, while butterflies have slightly more adventurous tastes, going for oranges and yellows, as well as reds and pinks. And bats and moths, uninfluenced by colour, have their own nocturnal favourites, invariably white, but always powerfully scented.

Bees collect nectar for energy and gather pollen in large yellow masses on their rear legs to provide protein for their brood (young larvae).

Marked for success

Flowers that have been photographed with cameras that imitate bee vision are often very strongly patterned with stripes, spots and concentric rings that seem to act as runway lights to the bees, showing them where to go to get the nectar, and, in passing, to brush against and collect the pollen. The colour we see is not always crucial in bee terms: although their range of vision naturally inclines them to blues and violets, they may extend to other colours if the pattern guides are strong enough. For example, bees love some

▲ The vivid yellow evening primrose, *Oenothera biennis* (left), is seen by insects by its ultraviolet image (right) showing the 'nectar guide'.

bright red penstemons and dahlias – even though we know that bees cannot see red – because the patterns and markings that the flowers offer are strong enough to attract them without the extra stimulus of visual (to the bee, that is) colour.

Gentian beardtongue,
Penstemon gentianoides

A Bees do not see colour like people do. They can see ultraviolet light and a range of blues, yellows, greens and violets, but they cannot see red. So a bee's eye view of many familiar flowers is very different to what you see.

How do plants with seedless fruit reproduce?

CLEMENTINES, NAVEL ORANGES and other citrus fruit are often advertised as 'seedless' in the shops. Obviously they are easier to eat – no pips to spit out – but, without seeds, how do they make new trees?

Parthenocarpic fruits have some disadvantages. The hormones that make fruit swell are present only in fertilised seeds, so parthenocarpic fruits are usually quite small (a tendency that can be overcome if the breeder doses the plant with artificial hormones, which will make the fruit bigger). And the lack of seeds means that growers must make new stock by grafting. The popularity of seedless fruit, though, outweighs these comparatively minor drawbacks.

There are other types of seedless fruit, but they do not all come about in the same way. Seedless grapes, for example, occur by a different process. Pollination does occur, and the fruit contains set seed, but a genetic mutation means that the seed does

Seedless citrus fruits come from parthenocarpic, or 'virgin-birth' trees: that is, trees that bear fruit without needing pollination. This is useful to growers – it is a stage they do not need to worry about.

not grow or develop the hard coating it needs for protection; instead, it simply withers away, leaving pipless fruit.

The most popular eating pear grown in Europe, 'Conference', has a natural tendency to set parthenocarpic fruits, so can crop even when a bad-weather season means that natural pollination may have been limited. And breeders can help the process on by treating plants with a particular natural hormone – gibberellic acid – which promotes any tendency to parthenocarpy.

◀ Conference' pears usually contain seeds, as shown here, and are pear-shaped. Fruits set without pollination have vestigial seeds and are elongated, rather than pear shaped.

Why do flowers smell?

How a flower smells comes from both the number of scent molecules it contains and the proportions they are arranged in. Not only that, but the scent is mutable – a flower can change both its strength and its quality at different times and for different reasons.

To humans, most flowers smell delicious, and gardeners never tire of sniffing their plants. But, for the plants themselves, scent is a key weapon in their competitive battle for survival. Night flowers, such as lilies, *Lilium*, tobacco plants, *Nicotiana*, and night-scented stocks, *Matthiola*, are famously fragrant, as their night-time pollinators will not see showy colours after dark. Daytime flowers, meanwhile, vary in their style of scent: species that are pollinated by bees and flies often have very sweet scents, while those that rely on beetles for their pollination tend much more towards musky, spicy aromas.

Flowering tobacco, *Nicotiana sylvestris*, has white flowers with a marked, sweet night scent typical of plants that depend on nocturnal moths for pollination.

Scent is just one of the ways in which flowers attract pollinators. It is particularly important for those that are adapted to nocturnal visitors, such as moths and bats, for whom colour will have less appeal than smell.

It's hard for us to look at a flower garden and see a battle for survival taking place. To plants, though, how well they have adapted to reproduce is a matter of life and death. And all their weapons are minutely graded and measured, whether they consist of colour, structure – or scent.

What is the difference between a fruit and a vegetable?

ARE FRUIT AND VEGETABLES DISTINGUISHABLE because of the different uses to which we put them in the kitchen? Or is there a fail-safe way of identifying them outside our subjective judgement of them as foodstuffs? As usual with plants, the answer has a degree of 'it depends'.

Essentially, a fruit has seeds and a vegetable does not. Certain anomalies, such as seedless grapes, immediately undermine the simplicity of this explanation, so it is more accurate to say that fruits arise from the ovaries of a plant, while all the other parts of the plant – flower buds, stalks, leaves and roots – count as vegetables.

Apart from this technical distinction, the everyday way of distinguishing fruit from vegetables is the way in which we eat them. Fruits that are generally used as vegetables make up a large category – technically aubergines, beans, courgettes, marrows, peas, peppers, pumpkins, squash and tomatoes are all fruits that we eat as vegetables, while rhubarb is a vegetable, but eaten as a fruit. Culinary definitions do not abide by botanical categories! Not only that, but different cuisines naturally vary in what is regarded as a vegetable and what a fruit; melons, for example, are treated as a vegetable in a number of Asian cuisines.

◀ Aubergines produce firm fruits, classed botanically as berries (see opposite), containing many seeds.

WHEN IS A BERRY NOT A BERRY?

Even more confusing is the botanical definition of a berry, which is quite different from the colloquial one. Technically, a berry is the product of a single flower, in which the outer wall of the plant's female organ – the ovary – develops into a pulpy, edible layer. This means that avocados and tomatoes are true berries, while raspberries and strawberries are not.

What are they, then?
A strawberry is the receptacle for the tiny seeds that dot its surface and that release plant hormones that allow the strawberry 'fruit' to ripen. Each raspberry, on the other hand, is the fused product of several ovaries that were originally contained within the same flower, and is what is known as an aggregate fruit. Each little divided unit of a raspberry is a berry in its own right, containing an individual seed. These small separate units, each with its own skin and seed, mean that the raspberry is an unusually rich source of fibre when eaten.

Avocado,
Persea americana

Strawberry,
Fragaria × *ananassa*

Raspberry,
Rubus idaeus

Why do flowers make nectar?

IF YOU ASKED A BEE WHY IT VISITS A FLOWER, it would not reel off a worthy description of its role as a pollinator. It would have a one-word answer: nectar. Without the reward of this sugary bribe, the bee would not spend its time going from flower to flower – and neither would most other insects.

Nectar is the flower's main attraction for almost all pollinating insects. The plant's scent and colour act as an advertising system to these insects: 'nectar available here'.

Nectar production comes at a high cost for the plant, using more than a third of most plants' available sugar resources. It is produced in nectaries, specialised glands that are usually – though not always – located within the flower of the plant. The nectaries are plumbed into the phloem tubes of the plant's vascular system so that sugars from the sap of the plant can be routed directly into them.

Key timing
Nectar is only necessary when the parent plant has pollen that it needs to be transported to another flower, so the flower releases scent and makes nectar available to visiting insects only when its pollen is ripe.

▲ In the Americas, hummingbirds, here scissor-tailed hummingbirds, are important pollinators. They require several times their own weight (up to 8g) of nectar each day.

The nectar itself is made to different recipes, according to the plant's key pollinator – mainly composed of glucose, fructose and sucrose, although the balance varies. Sucrose-rich nectar, for example, is mostly found in flowers that are pollinated by hummingbirds or insects with specialised long tongues, such as butterflies, moths and some long-tongued bees, while glucose and fructose seems to appeal most strongly to flies, short-tongued bees and bats. Each plant knows which recipe will have the strongest appeal to its specific pollinators.

When the plant has been fertilised or its pollen has all been used up, nectar production ceases. There's no longer any need to waste precious resources, and it has more important tasks to work on, such as ripening its seeds. This efficient use of resources is key to survival in the surprisingly ruthless world of plants.

POLLEN EATERS

 There are exceptions to every rule, and a few insects eat the pollen, rather than collecting it. Specialised beetles and mites favour pollen as a key part of their diet; ladybirds also enjoy it. Pollen is rich in protein and amino acids, so it is a valuable food; some species of wasps and bees have learnt to mix pollen with nectar to make a specially enriched food for their young.

▼ The long delicate proboscis (tongue) of the butterfly is ideal for removing nectar from daisy family plants such as zinnia, *Zinnia*, composed of numerous florets.

Is it true that sunflower heads follow the sun?

THERE'S A LONG-HELD PIECE OF gardener's lore that claims that, wherever the sun is, the sunflower turns to face it. And while it is not completely accurate, there is a grain of truth in it.

A balancing act

Here is the science: during the day, the stem of the immature sunflower, *Helianthus*, grows more on the side away from the sun, which means that the flower buds tilt to face it – and by sunset, they are facing west. After the sun sets, however, the plant performs a balancing act, as the other side of the stem grows, so that, by morning, the buds and opening sunflowers will be facing east again. It has been calculated that, by turning in this way, the still-growing flowers can make use of up to 15 per cent more sunlight to help them photosynthesise.

SUN WORSHIPPERS

Some plants really do follow the sun, a phenomenon called heliotropism. They tend to grow in harsh environments, in which just a little extra warmth may make the difference between successful seed setting and reproductive failure.

Sunflowers in the bud do face the sun; it is a way of maximising photosynthesis while the plant is in active growth. Once the flowers are mature and fully open, however, they turn to face east – and stay facing that way. This is worth bearing in mind if you are planting a sunflower border.

Common sunflower,
Helianthus annuus

Why are some hydrangeas blue and others pink?

FLOWER COLOUR CAN BE AFFECTED by a plant's surroundings, as well as by its own chemical make-up. *Hydrangea macrophylla* or *H. serrata* can both transform from blue to pink and back again, depending on the soil in which they grow.

Hydrangeas growing in soil with a high aluminium level will be blue, but the intensity of the blue will depend on the amount of anthocyanin pigment in the plant – the higher the pigment level, the deeper the blue colour. However, if there is not any aluminium in the soil, the hydrangea will be pink: again, just how deep a pink will depend on the quantity of pigment already in the plant.

The variable blue or pink colour depends on the inherent pigment level in the plant and the levels of aluminium in the soil. Aluminium is the key element; it is usually plentiful in acid soils but hardly present in alkaline or chalky ones.

Big-leaf hydrangea, *Hydrangea macrophylla*

HOW TO CHEAT

The grass-is-greener tendency in gardeners may mean that if you have blue hydrangeas you hanker after pink ones, and vice versa. If there is not enough aluminium in your garden to create blue flowers, you can water them with a solution of aluminium sulphate; conversely, if you have blue flowers and would prefer pink, you can add lime (calcium carbonate) to the soil around the base of the plant. A side effect of lime can be yellowing leaves, but this, too, can be countered by using a chelated fertiliser, which is usually applied directly to the affected leaves.

Why is there a glut of apples in one year, but then hardly any the next?

IS IT TRUE THAT FRUIT TREES have a year-on, year-off cycle for cropping and, if so, why? Why can they not produce a moderate crop every year? And is it just orchard trees that seem to experience this phenomenon, or does it apply to any cropping tree?

Apple trees have a tendency to lay down their flower buds early in the season, at the same time as the flowers are being pollinated and the fruits developing. This can work to their disadvantage – making fruit uses up a lot of the tree's resources, and there is sometimes little left to develop the next season's flowers, so that the following year the flowers are sparse and the fruit is disappointingly meagre. And this develops into a cycle; the small quantity of fruit in the bad year means that the tree can dedicate more of its energy to setting flowers for a generous harvest in the following season, and so on.

It is true that the one-year on, one-year off is a known pattern: it is called 'biennial bearing' and it is common to other trees, not just apples. It happens because a combination of factors sets up a cycle of good/poor harvests.

◀ Even the best-managed apple trees can have occasional gluts – an opportunity to make and freeze apple juice, dry apple slices and prepare chutney.

THREE WAYS TO ENCOURAGE AN APPLE TREE

In spring, tie down new, thin shoots. This fools the tree into thinking those branches are bearing fruit, and encourages it to set buds which will flower and fruit the next year.

Feed modestly – over-feeding usually encourages more leaves, rather than more fruit.

Do not prune. You are likely to end up with extra, and unwanted, growth (and you may even cut off the buds that will ultimately make next year's apples).

What is in it for the trees?

Apples are not the only trees to behave this way: other species, in particular beeches, *Fagus*, and oaks, *Quercus*, tend to have alternate good and bad years (in the case of these forest trees, a good year is called a 'mast' year). There is evidence in the case of oaks and beeches, which have many enthusiastic predators in the birds and animals who eat up their acorns and beech nuts, that in good years the crops are so heavy that there is an uneaten surplus which will survive as viable offspring, whereas in bad years the eaters will go hungry and hence their breeding will be adversely affected. So the trees have set up a balance in their natural situation.

This probably is not the reason for the good year/bad year alternation in apple trees. After all, apples 'want' their fruit to be eaten so that the seeds are carried away to colonise new territory. It is more likely that long-term breeding for high productivity in orchard trees has led to trees over-cropping and thus exhausting themselves.

Q Does bamboo die after flowering?

GARDENERS WHO VALUE THE STRIKING STRUCTURE of bamboo in their plots – and who have managed the tendency of plants in this group, which runs to more than a thousand species, to run wild into every corner of the garden – observe signs that their favourite is coming into flower with dismay: folklore says that, after it flowers, bamboo must die.

Although flowering in bamboos is dangerous for the parent plants, it may also be very rare: this group flowers very infrequently. It grows faster than almost any other plant but may flower only every decade or two – some bamboo groves have grown for more than a century without flowering. When it flowers, though, it does not stint: the foliage wilts and browns, and the plant produces huge masses of tall, feathery, grasslike heads full of seeds that are pollinated by the wind. It is not known quite why the sheer quantity of seed is so generous, but botanists have theorised that, by staging such a massive crop, bamboo is making sure that the animals that eat its seeds and shoots have a glut and will leave

◀ Common bamboo, *Bambusa vulgaris*, is a tropical species widely used for construction. It is reported to flower at 80-year intervals, producing no viable seed.

A It is true that flowering depletes bamboo more than most plants, but reports of its definite demise are exaggerated. Bamboo does not invariably die after flowering and, given care, it may recover.

enough of both untouched to ensure that some offspring survive. In those countries where bamboo is a crop plant, grown in large groves, all the plants tend to come into flower simultaneously.

The term for a plant that flowers once, sets seed and then dies is monocarpic; many popular succulents, such as *Aeonium* and *Aichryson*, share this trait.

▼ Bamboo is a woody grass. Grasses are herbaceous, while woody plants are trees and shrubs. It makes gardening sense to treat bamboo as a woody plant.

HOW TO SAVE BAMBOO

Firm horticultural action may save the day for your bamboo.

• If you spot any early flowering shoots, remove them immediately – this may discourage the plant from going into full flower.

• If it insists on flowering regardless, cut the clump back to ground level straight afterwards, and feed and water it.

• The following spring, apply a generous dose of a nitrogen-rich fertiliser.

With luck, fresh, green growth, free of flowers, will emerge from the base.

If all else fails, collect some of the seed from the flowers to plant again – cut off a few flowerheads and leave them in a paper bag to dry, then shake the seeds out.

How do plants produce such a variety of different colours?

THE 'HOW?' OF THE RAINBOW OF COLOURS that plants can make is just as important as the 'why?' More than three quarters of flowering plants depend on insect and animal pollinators and their biochemistry encourages them to maximise their chances. Colour is an important weapon in every flower's armoury.

In addition to their other skills, plants are chemists. They can mix up a huge range of pigment molecules to achieve a bewildering range of colours minutely calculated to have the strongest appeal to their chosen pollinator.

The ingredients that fix a flower's colour are a range of pigment molecules that divide into groups. Anthocyanins are behind red and blue flowers, the carotenoids give oranges and yellows, the betalains yield purple, and white and creamy shades come from anthoxanthins. The mixture of pigments that makes up the recipe for each flower can achieve subtle nuances that are found only in nature. Other factors can affect the final colour, too: for example, the pH balance of the soil can weigh in, altering the end result.

PAINTED TO PLEASE

The American author Michael Pollan has suggested that some plants have developed their flowers as much to appeal to people as to pollinators. The thinking, still at a speculative stage, goes that people are more likely to care for and cultivate a plant with beautiful flowers, thereby increasing its overall chances of survival.

◁ Sweet pea, *Lathyrus odoratus*, a pink-flowered Mediterranean annual, is, after more than 200 years of selection, now available in white, pink, blue, violet and red.

Why does pollen make some people sneeze?

IF YOU ARE SEIZED BY A SNEEZING FIT, how can you tell if it is pollen-related? Time of year may be a factor: pollen-induced sneezing is seasonal, so, if it is the middle of winter, pollen probably is not the culprit. On the other hand, if you are sneezing in repeated bouts, rather than an isolated sneeze or three, it is quite likely to be pollen's fault. And if you have a blocked nose and an itchy throat too, then a pollen allergy is probably to blame – sadly, the side effects extend beyond sneezing.

Many wind-pollinated grasses and trees release huge amounts of pollen because the potential wastage is so great. Most of the potentially irritating matter in the air around us is filtered out by the very fine hairs that line the human nose, but if the particles are small enough, like pollen, they may slip through. The fine dust can make you sneeze even if you do not have an allergy. If you are allergic, the effects can be considerably worse.

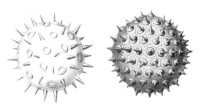

Pollen carries intricate markings unique to each species on the tough outer coat, or exospore. These markings can be seen under a scanning electron microscope.

Dust invaders

Certain molecules that exist in pollen have an extra irritant that causes a strong reaction in some people. Offenders are often found in the pollen of specific trees and grasses: the pollen of birch, *Betula*, trees, for example, is known to be particularly irritating because it contains especially potent protein molecules – specifically, the innocuous-sounding 'Bet v I'. Bet v I provokes a strong reaction in a victim's immune system – the system, which normally protects the body against infection, mistakes the pollen for an invading bug and swings into action, with very unwelcome results.

Pollen grains enter your mucus membranes as a very fine dust – irritating in their own right. If you suffer from an allergy, though, it is likely that specific pollen molecules will make things worse.

Are any flowers truly blue?

FLOWERS THAT ARE NATURALLY A TRUE, PURE BLUE
are rare. You may think that you have seen them, but when you
look closely at what colour they are, you will usually find that
the shade you thought of as blue is closer to something else
(look carefully at a bluebell, *Hyacinthoides*, for example, and
you will see that it has more than a hint of purple).

As usual, it is plant chemistry that dictates flower colours. Although there is not a pure blue pigment available to plants, they can overcome this to a certain extent by altering their internal chemistry.

Cornflower,
Centaurea cyanus

Around 10 per cent of flowers are blue or some approximation of it. Creating even a near-blue flower is a lot of effort for the parent plant. The closest pigments a plant can use to 'make' blue are anthocyanins, but in their natural state these create tints of red. In order to make a plant appear blue, they need an alkaline environment within the plant. Incredibly, plants can create that favourable environment for themselves, changing the pH of their sap to a high alkaline solution, and thus inducing the anthocyanins to show as blue in the flower, rather than the redder tints that show with a lower, more acid pH.

In agapanthus, *Agapanthus*, blue colours result from a complex between delphinidin and succinic acid (an organic acid). The blueness of hydrangeas is due to a complex of delphinidin (another organic acid) and aluminium. In the absence of aluminium, a red colour results. This is a common garden observation where adding aluminium sulphate to the soil promotes blue hydrangea flowers.

Delphinidin is the violet-blue pigment associated with blue larkspur, *Consolida*, and delphinium, *Delphinium*, whose 'blueness' is changed by the sap pH; the more alkaline the sap, the 'bluer' the flower colouring.

THE ELUSIVE BLUE ROSE

The holy grail for many growers would be a true blue rose, *Rosa*, a flower that does not exist in nature. Attempts to create one have been going on for several decades, and in theory, if plant breeders know which pigments and chemicals create blue, it should be possible. In 2008 'the first blue rose' was developed and heavily advertised by a Japanese company – but when the flower was unveiled, it was actually closer to a silvery lilac. The hunt for a blue blue rose continues.

Flower colour is just one part of a plant's pollination strategy, which also includes size, shape and attributes visible only to pollinators. Blue flowers appeal particularly to bees, but so do other colours. It is the combination of facets that is important.

Man-made blues

Artificial blues, though, are even more complex. The science that plant breeders now have at their disposal is sophisticated enough to add molecules to pigments and thus change a plant's natural colour.

Why do flowers close at night?

NOT EVERY FLOWER THAT CLOSES DOES SO AT NIGHT, but those that do may have a variety of reasons for doing so. A closed flower is protecting its delicate reproductive parts from a range of potential damage, from cold air, dew or even frost. It may also want to protect its pollen and nectar from night-flying insects that are not as effective with its specific needs as more favoured day pollinators.

The sugar switch

Just like humans, plants operate by a circadian rhythm, the internal clock by which you sleep at night and are awake during the day. These patterns appear to be triggered by light and darkness, which influence the genes that control the time-related activities of the plant. The times at which flowers open and close are remarkably precise –

Not all flowers close at night, but those that do, do so to protect their reproductive organs from cold damage and their pollen from undesirable night-flying pollinators.

probably because they have evolved to be open at the specific times when their favoured pollinators are most active. Not only can they tell the time, but they are also fast-acting: the plant can switch the genes that regulate the amount of sugar in its flowers' petals on and off. When the switch is on, the petals are rich in sugar and osmosis ensures more water flows into them – holding them open – but, when the switch is turned off, the amount of sugar reduces and the petals dehydrate and close up.

The common daisy, *Bellis perennis*, flower opens by day and closes by night – hence the name, 'day's eye'.

USING FLOWERS TO TELL THE TIME

Today, most floral clocks are simply flower beds planted in the shape of clock, and are popular in resorts as part of formal planting schemes. At best, they might incorporate a clock mechanism with moving hands that tell the time.

In the past, though, floral clocks could be much more elaborate – sometimes to an almost baroque level. In the 19th century, ambitious gardeners turned the extraordinary consistency of the times at which flowers opened and closed as the inspiration for clocks that actually told the time with flowers. A range of flowers would be carefully chosen so that they could be seen opening and closing all through the day and night, and set on the 'clock face' so that the moment of opening or closing matched the time slot on which they were placed. They cannot have been very accurate. Although flowers are mainly controlled by their own internal clocks, exterior factors, such as humidity and temperature, affect their performance, too – but they must have been entertaining to watch. One of the fanciest surviving designs, dating from 1822, was made up from 24 different kinds of plant, all in flower at the same time.

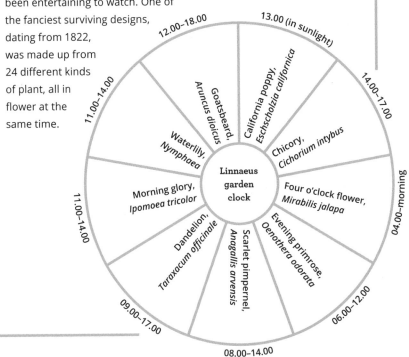

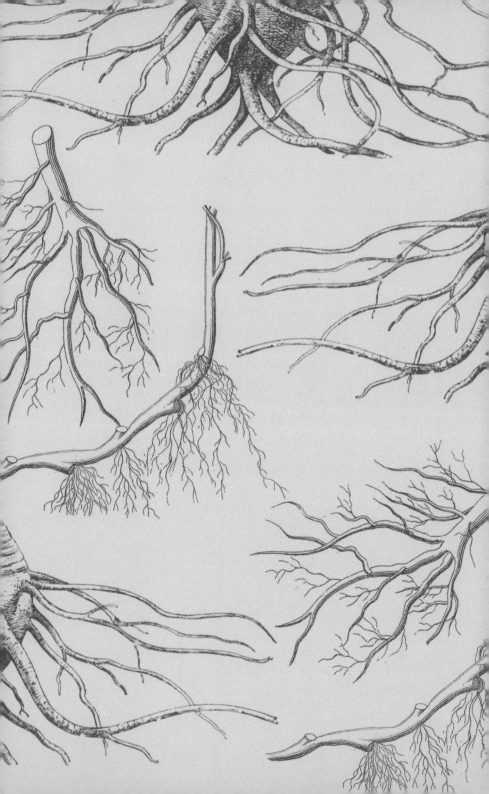

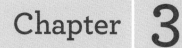

Chapter 3

Below the Ground

How do worms work?

IT SEEMS DISRESPECTFUL to refer to worms, of which there are many thousands of species besides the garden ones, as a tube with a mouth at one end and, well, you can guess what is at the other. But that is essentially what they are. Two worms are especially familiar in the garden, earthworms and brandlings; they are found in the soil and compost bins respectively.

Worms take in organic matter, such as leaves, through their mouths and digest them in the 'gut' that runs from one end of their segmented body to the other.

Like all animals, worms must breathe, which they do through their skin (this must always be moist). They have a circulatory system that contains blood, which is supplemented by another system that moves fluids round their body. They have a central nervous system that controls muscles set in each segment, and each segment has bristles to grip the soil, and secretes mucus to ease the worm's passage. Just because they have no brain as such does not mean they are unsophisticated. Worms are amazingly mobile in the soil, not only do they make tunnels but they are also capable of seeking and handling food and making a hasty escape from predators.

The gardener's friend

Since Darwin, scientists have confirmed the importance of worms in soil and shown that one of the benefits of the crucial gardening practice of feeding soil with compost and manure lies in the boost given to worm populations, which then permeate the soil with their burrows. Even small amounts of organic matter can increase worm populations out of all proportion – a feature now widely appreciated in no-dig gardening and no-till farming.

A worm is basically a tube that takes in organic matter at one end, digests it and deposits fertile material out the other end. It also breathes through its skin.

The periproct is the final segment, which includes the anus; the clitellum is part of the reproductive system used to deposit eggs; the segments feature bristlelike hairs used to anchor the body during movement; the prostomium is a fleshy lobe used as a sense organ and to seal the mouth when at rest.

SOME OTHER WORMY FACTS

- Worms are hermaphrodites, containing both male and female reproductive organs, but some worms need to mate with another worm for successful reproduction. This is accomplished by lying alongside each other and exchanging eggs and sperm.

- Worms can multiply to very great numbers in suitable conditions. According to research, there could be up to 432 worms, comprising seven main species, in 1m^2.

- Most worms 'eat' between 50 and 100 per cent of their body weight each day, though this varies from species to species.

- Unfortunately, the crucial question of does a worm severed by digging regrow into two worms remains only partially answered. The answer is 'sometimes', 'only certain species' or 'never', depending on which scientist you ask.

- Worms have no brains as such, relying instead on a cluster of nerve cells called a cerebral ganglion. They react very rapidly to external stimuli such as heat, light, moisture, touch and vibration received via its ventral nerve cord.

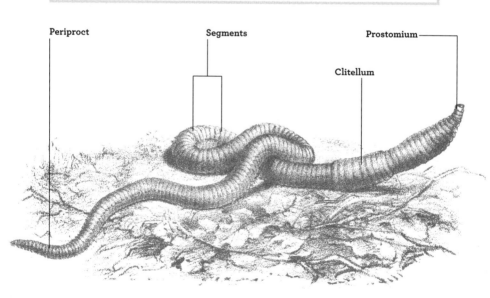

Periproct   Segments   Prostomium

Clitellum

Where do roots go?

ROOTS, TO GARDENERS, ARE A MYSTERY; how many are there, how widely do they spread and how deep? This is hardly surprising as roots growing in soil are embedded in a heavy, dense, wet, opaque material and to remove the soil to observe the roots immediately damages all but the coarsest roots. As a result, surprisingly little is known about roots despite their fundamental importance to plant growth and health. Gardeners take the understandable viewpoint, 'out of sight, out of mind'.

The 'business of being a plant', namely photosynthesis and reproduction, is conducted above ground, and it would make sense to keep roots to the minimum needed to anchor the plant, find water and minerals and a refuge from bad weather or accident. But roots are living things and need a constant supply of sugars from the leaves. In fact, the extent and nature of roots is just as finely tuned to the plant's environment as the shoots and foliage.

The old idea that the root mirrors the shape of a plant or tree is wrong. In truth, the size and shape of the root varies from plant to plant. Some grasses, for example, have long, deep roots, while hedges and trees tend to have shallow roots that spread out widely.

The tip of the iceberg

Small annual plants might be expected to have small roots and this is often the case: garden peas, onions and potatoes, for example, have very limited root systems. But other small plants can (soil conditions permitting) send roots very deeply. Turnips can reach down more than 80cm, ryegrass to 15cm and wheat to 12cm. Medium-sized perennial plants need and usually have moderate roots. Shrubs, for example, have a root spread of about the same as the canopy.

Unlike trees, shrubs are often routinely pruned, which disrupts the shoot–root balance.

Well-clipped hedges, no matter how tall, seldom have significant roots that reach further than 1m beyond the base of the hedge. The trees that make up the hedge would have substantial root systems if the above-ground growth were to be left unpruned.

THE ROOT OF THE PROBLEM

Trees have notoriously large and wide-ranging roots which can draw so much water out of the soil that the resulting soil shrinkage causes costly damage to buildings, walls and pipes. Tree roots spread to wherever there is water, air and soil that is not too hard. Leaky, shallow drainage pipes, containing easily accessible water and air, are a magnet to tree roots.

Contrary to popular opinion, tree roots do not mirror the aerial architecture and spread mostly within the top 1m of soil, where there are the most nutrients and air. This 'plate-like' root formation can easily spread well beyond the height of the tree, and in some particularly invasive species, notably poplars, *Populus*, and willows, *Salix*, extend up to three times the height of the tree.

Having said that, where the soil is deep enough and root growth is not restricted by hard, acid or waterlogged soil, some root growth will plunge deeper in search of moisture.

False

True

Q Why does rainwater turn the soil acid?

CARBON DIOXIDE OCCURS NATURALLY IN THE ATMOSPHERE, lowering the pH of rainwater from a neutral 7 to something more acidic, often around the 5.5 mark. Pollution can push this down further – man-made CO_2 and other pollutants, such as sulphur dioxide and nitrogen oxide, may be added to the mix – and the resulting phenomenon is known as acid rain.

Countering acid

When soil contains limestone or chalk particles, its natural calcium carbonate – alkaline – levels are so high that acid rain is neutralised. Soils rich in clay, too, have alkaline reserves, which buffer them from the immediate effects of acid rain. On sandy soils, however, the effects of the rain are felt fast, and they will quickly acidify.

High-acid soils are not good for growing things – on both agricultural land and gardens, regular applications of lime are needed to keep the soil fertile. Manures and composts are almost always very highly alkaline, and they can counter the effects of acidity.

Where land is not used for growing food, for example in wet, upland regions and on very sandy soils, the ground tends to remain acid, as too much lime would be needed to make neutralising it feasible – it would cost too much.

Although acid soils remain a problem, some man-made pollution has reduced over the last few decades. In areas where coal has been replaced as a fuel, pollution by sulphur (which is highly acidic) has grown much less – to the point that soil, which needs some sulphur, has become deficient. Soil management is simply a question of maintaining a balance, with elements added or subtracted to keep soils as fertile as possible.

A Rainfall is local, and its effect on the ground depends a good deal on the sort of soil it falls on. If the ground is alkaline, it can work against the acid in rain, neutralising it; if the soil already has a tendency to acidity, then, sooner or later, the soil will acidify.

Does the answer really lie in the soil?

A POPULAR COMEDY RADIO SHOW back in the 1950s featured a wise old Somerset farmer, with an accent to match, whose gnomic response to any question – about anything – was 'the answer lies in the soil'. He embodied the traditionalist who believed that everything will be well if you just take proper care of the land – but was he right?

Soil babysits plants

Soil is crucial to growth in a number of ways. Plant growth depends on an adequate supply of water, and the soil can store huge quantities during rainy periods to sustain a crop during the drier months. Soil helps to maintain the temperature plants need, too: in spring, it heats up to encourage root growth, then protects the roots from excessive heat in summer. In cold regions, it even provides protection from winter frosts.

Yes. The productivity of the soil dictates the success of the human food supply, either in terms of the plants it grows or the creatures that eat them. So far, despite the investment of quite a lot of energy and creativity, no viable substitute as a growing medium has been either found or invented.

SOIL HEROES

Soil plays a crucial part in its own right, but it is also home to a number of environmental heroes, including microbes (not for nothing is soil known as 'the poor man's rainforest'); earthworms, which aerate and enrich the soil; and fungi, which are accomplished biochemists that transform unrotted organic matter into plant foods and humus.

How long does a dead tree stand?

A DEAD TREE THAT IS STILL STANDING can fall at any time, particularly if root disease has rotted away the roots, leaving the tree top-heavy. However, trees that die of other causes can stand for as long as 100 years. In urban areas and on managed land, dead trees are often removed for safety reasons. But because dead trees support much wildlife, there is a good case for managing them by reducing their height and spread.

Trees, such as birch, *Betula*, or spruce, *Picea*, which are not very durable, rot quickly and remain standing for only a year or two. More resilient genera with notably harder or resinous timber, such as pines, *Pinus*, and oaks, *Quercus*, can remain upright for a decade. Trees fall sooner in wet, mild climates than in dry, cold ones. If the tree was killed by honey fungus, the roots will soon decay and the tree may fall very soon after it shows signs of ill-health.

Depending on the climate, and the condition of the roots and wood, a dead tree, or 'snag', can stand for as little as two years or for many decades.

To fell or not to fell

Gardeners are sometimes loath to lose the height, shelter and privacy of a tree, and when it dies they may choose to clothe its bare branches with a honeysuckle, *Lonicera*, clematis, *Clematis*, or climbing rose, *Rosa*. This can look attractive; however, it increases the 'sail' area, meaning that it catches the wind more readily than the bare dead branches would, making the tree more likely to be blown down.

Not every dead tree is blown down; many break above ground because of the weakening action of bracket fungi and other fungi that rot trunks. Reducing height and branch spread can limit risk.

Where dead trees are unlikely to cause harm by falling – in open fields or woodland, for example – they are often left to do so naturally, as the decaying tree supports much wildlife. When they do eventually tumble, the remaining roots will pull up a substantial mass of soil, leaving a pit. Once it has come to rest on the moist soil, the branches and trunk rot away much faster than when the tree was standing. However, the pit persists for many, many years, leading to the pitted surface typical of ancient forests.

FIVE THINGS THAT LOVE DEAD TREES

Stag beetle (*Lucanus cervus*) A very large beetle characterised by its antlerlike jaws. Flies at night. Its bulbous larvae feed on rotting wood.

Crested tit (*Parus cristatus*) This bird will make its nest in a hole in a rotting stump. In the UK it is restricted to the ancient pine forests of Scotland.

Noctule bat (*Nyctalus noctula*) These bats lie up by day in dead trees before going out 'hawking' at night.

Stag beetle,
Lucanus cervus

Woodlice (*Porcellio scaber*) They feed on rotting wood, but must have damp conditions as they are crustacea (like crabs or lobsters). They are sometimes feared by gardeners as pests but are generally innocent.

Chicken of the woods (*Laetiporus sulphureus*) A bright yellow, edible fungus that feeds on dead timber.

Woodlice,
Porcellio scaber

Why do toadstools often grow under trees?

THERE IS A FAINTLY FANTASTICAL QUALITY in the sight of toadstools growing around the base of a tree – but it is not a picturesque accident. It is quite common for toadstools and trees to live together in a symbiotic relationship: the toadstools are just the visible evidence of what is going on underground.

Keeping it in the family

There are plenty of benefits when trees and fungi make friends. The tree exchanges the sugars made by photosynthesis in its leaves for minerals and water collected by the fungus. The mat of the mycorrhizal filaments of the fungus has a huge spread underground, and its very thin threads, hyphae, are much finer and more numerous than the tree's roots, and so offer a much greater area for mineral absorption. Key minerals such as phosphorus, needed in large quantities by trees, pass across from the hyphae into the roots.

The relationship is not just useful; in poor soils, it is essential. While a tree in a cultivated garden or park situation may be able to pull enough nutrients from the enriched soil on its own, in a more competitive environment it actually needs the greater underground spread offered by the fungus to survive.

Do not assume that every fungus seen beneath a tree is benign: honey-coloured toadstools may be a sign that honey fungus is at work underground, colonising and feeding on the tree's roots without giving anything back. It is the commonest killer of garden trees, and is also destructive in forests, plantations and orchards.

Many fungi live in close and mutually beneficial association with the roots of trees. In the autumn, the mycorrhizal structures underground support their own long-distance reproduction by sending up toadstools that will release fertile spores.

FIVE TREE-LOVING FUNGI

There are three delicious examples, plus two that you should not even think about eating:

Black summer truffle,
Tuber aestivum

Black summer truffle, *Tuber aestivum*, in a relationship with oak, *Quercus*, or hazel, *Corylus*, trees. An expensive delicacy sometimes found wild in the UK.

Chanterelle, *Cantharellus cibarius*, likes to live with broadleaved trees. An orange, slightly funnel-shaped fungus with a delicious, delicately floral flavour.

Chanterelle,
Cantharellus cibarius

Cep, *Boletus edulis*, is friendly with oak trees. A rounded, brown fungus with a dense, almost meaty flavour. Great in stews.

Cep,
Boletus edulis

Fly agaric, *Amanita muscaria*, likes birch, *Betula*, trees. A red cap with white spots, like the poisonous toadstool from a fairy tale. Highly toxic if eaten, with hallucinogenic properties.

Fly agaric,
Amanita muscaria

Cedar cup, *Geopora sumneriana*, a natural partner for cedar, *Cedrus*, and yew, *Taxus*, trees. A large, cup-shaped fungus which splits into a star shape when mature. Toxic if eaten.

Cedar cup,
*Geopora
sumneriana*

How much of a plant is in its roots?

THERE IS A RECOGNISED EQUATION in botanical matters, called the root–shoot ratio, which calculates the weight of the underground part of the plant against the combined weight of the stem or trunk, branches and leaves – and it varies a good deal according to which type of plant you are considering.

Roots and shoots

You might think that a big tree would need a big root system, and this is true to a point – if its roots were too puny, it would be easy to topple. As a proportion of the whole tree, though, the root mass is small – the top part, the 'shoot', weighs five times as much as the roots. The tree needs light, and, particularly in a wood or forest, it is in competition with its neighbours, so investing in growing its trunk and branches to reach towards the sun is a worthwhile use of resources.

On the other hand, grasses keep most of their resources in their roots – four fifths of grass's weight is underground. Why? Because most grasses have evolved to be grazed, and, unlike trees, need the resources to renew and regrow constantly. While they are not competing for light, they need to be more competitive underground, in the search for water and nutrients.

Given good conditions, seedling root–shoot ratio (here coneflower, *Echinacaea purpurea*) is balanced, but under poor soil conditions roots can be reduced.

Perhaps surprisingly, trees, proportionally, hold far less mass in their roots than does grass. To make sense of this, you need to think in terms of investment: every plant invests in those parts that are most likely to support its long-term survival.

Is it worth ridding soil of stones?

TRADITIONAL GARDENING LORE holds that you should meticulously remove all sizeable stones from any ground you are planning to cultivate. How important this is depends on the crops you are planning to plant – and also whether or not you like the look of immaculately raked soil, or are happy with something that appears more rough and ready.

WHEN YOU SHOULD – AND WHEN YOU NEED NOT BOTHER

DO

• **Lawns** – remove all stones and rake well before planting seed or you will get a bumpy lawn that may throw stones up and break your mower.

• **Raised beds** – the whole point is that they are filled with the best soil. Be meticulous.

DO NOT

• **When you are laying turf** – ready-made, rather than grown-from-seed lawns need only the most cursory stone-picking.

• **When you are planting larger shrubs** – they will cope with stony soil.

How fussy plants are about stones tends to depend on their natural habitat: some alpines, for example, have their natural homes on scree. But if you want good cropping or generous flowering from annuals or tender perennials that need plenty of water and nutrients, you should put the work in and try to remove the stones from their rooting zone – which means the top 30cm of soil.

Most trees are tolerant of stones, while, as a group, shrubs are the toughest members of the plant family, many able to scratch a living on the most inhospitable soil. If you want a vegetable or flower garden, though, it is worth removing stones before you plant.

Q If I stood under a tree in a storm, would I feel its roots move?

FIRST THINGS FIRST, NEVER STAND under a tree in a storm. Quite apart from the danger of falling branches (or, in extreme cases, the whole tree), a tall tree will often be the highest object in the vicinity, so will act as a great target for a lightning strike. If you are unlucky, the lighting will 'spot' your superior conductive qualities, leave the tree and jump over to you.

The root plate of a tree can spread out across an area one-and-a-half times the height of the tree, giving it a broad base to absorb the strains of a high wind. The leverage imposed on the base of the tree by the movement of its foliage, branches and trunk is offset by the plate, which is composed of a mass of soil held together by twisting roots that also wrap themselves around rocks for support.

A Let us look at the question hypothetically. Yes, if you stood under a large tree while a full storm gale was blowing, you would probably feel the soil moving underneath you as the swaying tree transferred the mechanical stress on the trunk to the roots.

Not infallible

Despite this strong base, however, trees do fall in high winds. It is far more usual for them to uproot – pulling the root plate up with them as they fall – than simply to break in two. During Hurricane Sandy, the famously destructive storm that was the high – or, rather, low – point of the 2012 North American hurricane season, nearly 8,500 uprooted trees were recorded in New York City alone. And it does not always take a hurricane to do the damage.

WHY TREES FALL

The commonest reason for a tree uprooting is windthrow. This is the phenomenon when the trunk of the tree acts as a lever on the root plate and the stress proves too much for the latter – so the tree falls, pulling the whole plate up with it. The tallest trees are, on the whole, the most susceptible, although trees in built-up areas may also suffer because their roots, thwarted by building foundations and other blocks, have not been able to stretch out as broadly as they naturally would. Another factor is how wet the soil is – trees planted in reliably damp earth will not have had to reach for water, so their roots will tend to be shallower than those of trees growing in arid conditions.

Storms are good, too, at seeking out previously unseen areas of rot in trees. Wood decay may weaken a tree's structure, causing uneven stresses, which expose weak points in high winds. While they may not bring the whole tree down, these stresses may tear and rip branches from the main trunk.

'Ball and socket' failure occurs where the root ball pivots. The canopy acts as a sail in gales, exerting leverage on a constricted root ball.

Could a tree drink a swimming pool?

USUALLY, TREES ARE NOT ALLOWED to drink swimming pools. Being lined with concrete or fibreglass, the pools are not accessible to a tree's thirst and, even if a pool springs a leak, it will not generally be extensive enough to allow a tree to drink its fill. But if a tree had unfettered access to a pool, would it be able to drain it dry?

A tree's uptake of water is not really 'drinking' in the human sense, though – the transpiration process means that the tree is discharging around 90 per cent of the water it takes up straight back into the atmosphere. Only the ten per cent left over remains in the tree, and is used to maintain its system and to promote growth. If a swimming pool were to spring a leak, the water would be an attraction to any tree's roots, but, since roots also need oxygen, they would not be able to grow directly into the leak. A crack near the surface of the water might pose a greater risk, since the roots would have access to both water and air. Naturally occurring pools – unlined – often have large masses of tree roots growing into the water.

A favourite tipple

In terms of what trees like to drink, too, chlorinated pool water is not ideal. Chlorine is highly toxic, and a concentration as weak as 0.5 parts per million in pool water can harm a tree. It is far more poisonous during periods when the tree is actively growing, and some trees are particularly susceptible to chlorine poisoning – maple, *Acer*, horse chestnut, *Aesculus*, and ash, *Fraxinus*, trees all have an especially low tolerance.

▷ Horse chestnut, *Aesculus hippocastanum*, trees are widely grown trees, most well-known for producing conkers. They are highly susceptible to chlorine poisoning.

SIX THIRSTY TREES AND SIX MODEST DRINKERS

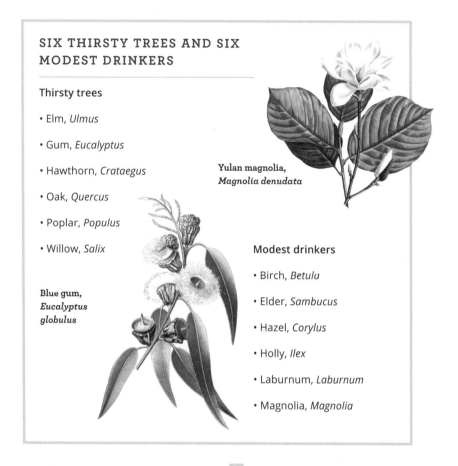

Thirsty trees

- Elm, *Ulmus*
- Gum, *Eucalyptus*
- Hawthorn, *Crataegus*
- Oak, *Quercus*
- Poplar, *Populus*
- Willow, *Salix*

Yulan magnolia,
Magnolia denudata

Blue gum,
*Eucalyptus
globulus*

Modest drinkers

- Birch, *Betula*
- Elder, *Sambucus*
- Hazel, *Corylus*
- Holly, *Ilex*
- Laburnum, *Laburnum*
- Magnolia, *Magnolia*

Break-ins

Generally, a tree's roots will not be able to do any damage to a swimming pool. Put a comparatively fragile, plastic pool liner alongside the very sharp and invasive roots of bamboo, however, and it is possible that the pool might suffer a breach. In a real-life situation, the pool's owner would do well to sink a strong plastic barrier at least 1m below the soil and extending a few centimetres above it between bamboo and pool.

A Large trees have been recorded as lifting as much as 450 litres of water from the ground in a day, so in terms of the volume of water a tree could potentially consume, the answer is yes. But given that chlorine is highly toxic to many trees, it wouldn't do them any good.

Why do stones rise to the surface after rain?

INEXPERIENCED GARDENERS SOMETIMES watch with dismay in spring as their freshly dug and raked plots become covered with stones after a few showers. Not only that, but having cleared away the unwanted 'crop', another lot of stones may appear the following year. Why does it happen – sometimes more than once?

A double crop

Not only that, but when you dig the soil again the following year, the process will repeat itself. Experienced gardeners and allotmenteers soon accept that raking the stones off the growing area after the first rains of spring is an annual chore.

Historically, this littering of stones could be helpful. They were an easily gathered resource that was often pressed into service for building work. In northern Britain, for example, the flat stones that came to the surface were used in the drystone walls characteristic of the area.

Stones are generally evenly distributed in soil, but the annual stir-up of cultivation redistributes them so that more are close to the surface. When the cultivated soil settles after rain, the stones become more readily apparent.

IT COULD BE WORSE

As you rake the stones from your growing space, consider this: in very cold climates, where the soil freezes annually, the frozen water in the soil expands, lifting it from below. The result is a bumper crop of stones after the first thaw every spring.

Even if gardeners rake soil regularly, stones will continue to reappear at the surface from a near inexhaustible supply in the subsoil.

When a tree catches fire, do its roots burn?

IN COOL NORTHERN CLIMATES, forest or bushfires are not a huge concern: they rarely occur and when they do, they do not usually cover huge areas of land. In other regions of the world, though, such as California or parts of Australia, they can pose a huge hazard, and ground fires can play a deadly part.

In the UK, most tree roots are too heavily insulated by soil, and the soil around them too damp, to allow them to catch fire, even if the tree they belong to is ablaze.

In hot, dry climates, though, roots can and do catch fire. Typically, a layer of dead material on the surface of the ground is set alight by a camp fire or a lightning strike. The burning litter sets the dry and shallow roots on fire and, under the right conditions, the blaze can travel underground, sometimes for quite large distances, smouldering for days, weeks or even months. Sometimes, these underground fires are detected by the smell of smoke as it seeps to the surface. Eventually, the sleeper fire will travel up to ground level and emerge, setting trees and shrubs alight, and sometimes launching a full-scale bushfire. Firefighters in regions where such fires are common know that they must dig over burnt areas to eradicate the fire underground.

PUTTING OUT A FIRE SAFELY

Every boy scout or girl guide once learnt how to put out a camp fire safely.

Now that it is less familiar knowledge, remember these key points:

- Put an outdoor fire out by pouring water on it.

- Never bury a fire – it can catch underground.

- Rake out the embers and make sure they are cool – if they are too hot to touch, they are too hot to leave.

How much damage can roots do?

THERE IS A LONG-ESTABLISHED NEAR-MYTH that plant roots can damage building foundations. Home owners tend to have an exaggerated view of just how much power tree roots, in particular, wield but, in reality, roots have quite a few limitations, needing both air and moisture to travel (there is more air than you might imagine underground) and usually opting to go around rather than through obstructions. Although it is not unknown for roots to cause problems, any damage is almost always done indirectly.

Subsidence happens when the foundations of a house do not rest on very strong or deep foundations and properly compacted soil. Because tree roots are opportunists, they will find their way into any available space, but the space has to be there first. Particular soils, specifically those heavy in clay, can shrink and swell quite dramatically in dry and wet weather respectively, and trees may exacerbate this natural tendency by extracting water from the soil as it swells, leading to particularly high levels of shrinkage. Gradually, the soil subsides as the amount of water it is

It is probably easier to list the damage that roots can't do. Roots do not tend to damage drains, paving, walls or house foundations. When roots do cause damage, it is not usually the result of a direct attack, but rather as the indirect result of subsidence.

receiving, even in wet weather, is not equal to the amount the roots are taking away – it is the subsidence that causes the structural damage.

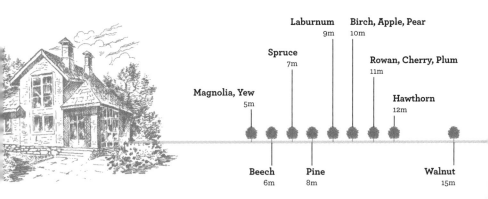

Magnolia, Yew
5m

Beech
6m

Spruce
7m

Pine
8m

Laburnum
9m

Birch, Apple, Pear
10m

Rowan, Cherry, Plum
11m

Hawthorn
12m

Walnut
15m

HOW DEEP SHOULD A TREE BE PLANTED?

How deep should you plant a tree? The idea that planting it deep in the ground (with the top of the rootball some distance below soil level) will make it easier for the tree to take up water is long-established and much debated between serious gardeners. As far back as 1618, the clergyman-gardener William Lawson, author of the popular *Country Housewife's Garden*, was already arguing strongly that deeper planting did not benefit trees. Science today supports him – trees tend to do better if they are planted 'level to grade' – that is, with the soil levelled just at the top of the rootball. When a tree is planted deep, this encourages its roots to grow upward, as they need air as well as water. Because the perfect mix of air and water is comparatively close to the surface, roots planted too deep struggle to reach the air and develop a tendency to grow around each other, rather than spreading out and creating a broad, healthy root plate for the tree to draw from. Healthy trees are planted shallow.

Soil line

Young tree ready for planting

It is a sensible precaution, even if the risk is not very high, to plant trees a reasonable way away from house walls. Some have much further reaching roots than others, so the recommended planting distances differ widely.

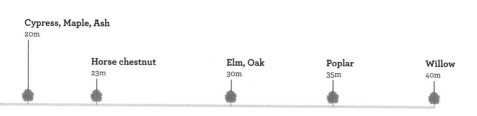

Cypress, Maple, Ash
20m

Horse chestnut
23m

Elm, Oak
30m

Poplar
35m

Willow
40m

How long do stumps last?

WHEREVER TREES GROW, sooner or later there will be stumps. Trees may die through disease, or be felled – either for timber or because they have grown too large for the space they are in. And once a tree is felled, the stump remains. If it is not grubbed up, though, how long will it be there?

Some other factors may discourage rot: occasionally, for example, the roots of a stump may have grafted underground with those of another, living tree, in which case the stump will continue to take up nourishment and may not rot at all. Some genera, such as pines, *Pinus*, 'fed' by nearby trees in this way, do not regrow from a felled stump but will continue to put on growth rings annually, just like a living tree. Still other tree types, such as willows, *Salix*, are not killed by felling, but readily regrow shoots from the stump.

Stumps can be a nuisance to gardeners and it can cost a good deal to have them grubbed out mechanically. If you want to speed the process up, the most effective way is to have the stump broken up or split, with a chainsaw or by means of hammering in wedges; this increases the surface areas susceptible to fungi and other organisms that encourage rot.

Timber stumps can prove remarkably resilient despite the fact that they are usually in an ideal environment for decay – damp soil, offering plenty of opportunities for fungi, insects and microbes, all of which foster rot.

Creating a stumpery

Victorian gardeners loved themes, and one popular feature they often undertook was an ornamental stumpery. These consisted of small areas of stumps around which ferns and other woodland species could be cultivated; even as the stumps rotted, interesting fungi and mosses would appear on and around them. Originally, stumperies seem to have been started in areas where trees had been felled and there were already collections of stumps, but, as their popularity grew, keen gardeners would actually import logs and stumps to get the effect in their own gardens. If you want to try a stumpery corner in your own garden, whether you are using existing stumps or buying in the wood, try giving the surfaces a brush with natural yoghurt – this will encourage mosses and lichens to colonise them speedily.

If a rock garden doesn't appeal, consider a stumpery. The principle is the same: a well-drained site for delicate plants. Woodland plants, especially ferns, are popular stumpery plants.

TIMETABLE TO DECAY

How long a stump takes to rot also depends on which type of tree it is – trees vary enormously according to the density of their wood, and to how rot-resistant they are.

Here is how long you might expect the stumps of six popular genera to last before they rot away completely:

- **Birch,** *Betula* 40–45 years
- **Spruce,** *Picea* 55–60 years
- **Pine,** *Pinus* 60–65 years
- **Ash,** *Fraxinus* 75 years
- **Cherry,** *Prunus* 75 years
- **Oak,** *Quercus* 100+ years

When annuals die back each winter, do their roots die back, too?

ANNUALS ARE OFTEN THE SHOWY BUT SHORT-LIVED STARS
of the garden – they grow, set seed and die, all within a single
season. Perennials, on the other hand, die back, but reappear the
following year, ready to undertake the cycle again. But what is
happening underground? Do annuals die away altogether?

Perennial vs. annual

Unlike annuals, herbaceous perennial
plants can live for years. Nevertheless,
they do not always retain all their roots
over winter; unlike trees, they do not
need them for support. Perennials,
therefore, usually let some of their
roots die back while they are dormant,
retaining enough to fuel growth when
spring returns.

Strawberries, *Fragaria*, offer a good
example of a typical perennial's cycle
of growth. During late winter and early
spring, the plant invests plenty of

When annuals die, they are
gone – the whole plant is dead.
Below ground their roots rot
over the winter, leaving
nutrients to feed other plants
over the following year, and
gaps in the soil that will help
its aeration and drainage.

resources into growing its roots,
but by late spring the balance is
shifting, with more energy going into
developing flowers and growing fruit,
and some of the roots die off.

After the strawberry plant has
cropped, the foliage predominates
through the rest of the summer, with
the roots continuing to die back until,
by autumn, the strawberry has only its
persistent roots left. Although by now
these comprise only a small proportion
of the plant, they will begin to grow
again over the winter, preparing for a
burst of activity when spring comes.

Strawberry,
Fragaria vesca

What is a water table?

WHEN RAIN FALLS, it begins what is known as the water cycle. Rainwater drains away, flowing into drainage pipes or ditches that deposit it into streams and rivers. Some rain is absorbed and sinks down through porous rocks, such as chalk or sandstone, to saturated underground areas called aquifers, which, in turn, feed springs that feed streams. Rivers flow into the sea from where some water evaporates, forming clouds, which then fall as rain, completing the cycle.

An underground ebb and flow

As you would expect, the level of the water table rises in winter and sinks in summer. It can respond quite quickly to heavy rain, and heavy prolonged rain can sometimes mean that the water table rises fast enough to cause surface flooding. It is closest to the surface near water-filled ditches and rivers, but, on chalk or sandy soils that are not near rivers, the saturated area is very much deeper. Although you might mentally picture a water table as flat, where the ground slopes the water table will run more or less parallel with the surface of the soil and is actually flowing – very slowly – downhill, through the porous ground.

Wells can be sunk to extract water from the water table, and are shallow where it is high, but, to get water from aquifers, very deep boreholes are drilled. These punch through the water table to access water from the more stable source below.

Under all soil there will be an area saturated with rainwater. The water table is the level below which the ground is saturated. How near the surface it is varies quite a lot from place to place and season to season.

When two plants' roots meet underground, do they help or hinder each another?

IT CAN GET QUITE CROWDED UNDERGROUND, and it is inevitable that the roots of one plant will encounter those of another (or quite a few others) as they stretch themselves to full capacity. When they meet, are they helpful to one another, do they engage in a fight for more space or do they simply ignore each other?

Brief encounters

Above the ground, the aerial parts of plants are seldom in close enough long-term contact to graft with each other. Gardeners sometimes induce them to graft – a process called 'approach grafting' – by binding two branches together, but it will not happen by accident. Under the ground, though, it is another matter.

Roots growing in a solid, dense medium move only very slowly, and when they meet may be pressed

Roots of different plant species compete as a general rule. However, root grafting (when two roots fuse with one another to become a single root) is common in nature, especially between plants of the same species.

together by the soil around them. A root graft is not just two roots growing together in close proximity, it is two roots actually fusing into a single unit. When trees are joined at the roots they can share water and nutrients. Unfortunately, some diseases can also be transferred through grafted roots – it is believed that Dutch elm disease may be spread this way, as well as by bark-dwelling beetles. It may also be possible for weedkiller, applied to one tree or a stump, to spread to another if it shares a root system.

Occasionally, plants of different species will spontaneously graft their roots, but this is a rare occurrence. More commonly, root grafting will unite two plants of one species, enabling a strong tree, for example, to sustain its weaker neighbour, and both trees to close gaps into which competitor species might move.

PLANT WARFARE

Some plant roots turn nasty underground – they have developed their own chemical weaponry to fight off rival trees.

The roots of the black walnut, *Juglans nigra*, secrete a potent toxin called juglone, which can inhibit respiration in some other plants, including apples, *Malus*, or tomatoes, *Solanum lycopersicum*. The toxin can affect plants across the full root spread, which may reach outward as far as three times the height of the tree.

Tree-of-heaven, *Ailanthus altissima*, has roots that are thought to exude a molecule called ailanthone, which is toxic to other plants. This has made it a serious invasive pest in many regions.

The shrubby New Zealand tea tree, *Leptospermum scoparium*, secretes a chemical inhibitor – a molecule called leptospermone – which has actually been synthesised and marketed as a commercial weedkiller.

Black walnut,
Juglans nigra

Tree-of-heaven,
Ailanthus altissima

New Zealand tea tree,
Leptospermum scoparium

QWhere does topsoil end and subsoil begin?

TOPSOIL IS DARK, CRUMBLY, SWEET SMELLING AND RICH in worms and roots. Below this top layer is the subsoil, usually a clearly defined section made up of paler and more solid material, with few roots or worms present. And beneath the subsoil lies the underlying geological material for each region: for example, clay or rock.

In cultivated soils, the topsoil is often around the depth of the tool that cultivates it – perhaps the blade of a spade or plough – around 20–25cm. In undisturbed, uncultivated soil, the arrangement may be more complex.

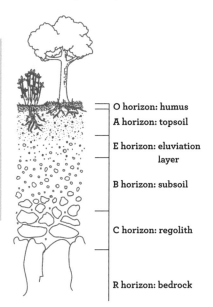

O horizon: humus
A horizon: topsoil

E horizon: eluviation layer

B horizon: subsoil

C horizon: regolith

R horizon: bedrock

Soil horizons are used to classify soils by soil scientists. A garden soil inspection is invaluable in choosing what to plant.

The horizons in soil

The layers of soil going down to the groundrock are called horizons. In uncultivated soils, there may be as many as six layers, and soil scientists, or pedologists, identify each with a letter (confusingly for the novice, they are not in alphabetical order).

The top layer is the O horizon. In a typical soil this might be made up of organic matter, derived from plant foliage that is not yet decomposed: in a forested area, this would be fallen leaves, but, in a wet region, it might be waterlogged and peaty – low in oxygen, so especially slow to decompose.

Below the O horizon is the topsoil, also known as the A horizon. This is the fertile layer, dark, crumbly and well worked by earthworms and other soil animals, and is where seeds germinate and roots grow. In wet climates, minerals, such as iron and aluminium, wash out of the topsoil and accumulate below the A horizon, creating a pale, silty layer which does not encourage plant growth – not useful from either the agricultural or the horticultural point of view. This is the E horizon. (Sometimes there is no distinct E horizon, and the B layer comes directly under the A horizon.)

Next down is the B, subsoil, horizon. This is pale, due to a lack of organic matter, and is also harder and less permeable than the topsoil layers. It is made up of accumulations of clay, with accretions of iron and aluminium. The subsoil layer is often ill-drained and airless: if you were to dig that far down, you would find that it was grey and smelled sour – clear indications that it will not be hospitable to plant roots.

Below B comes the C horizon, which is composed of the 'parent' material of the soil – typically gravel, clay or other deposits. By now, you are quite deep underground, and this layer is unaffected by any of the weathering processes that influence the formation of the higher layers. Last of all is the R horizon. This is formed of the bedrock of the area.

Modern soil management practices aim to mimic the structure of the natural horizons and avoid too much soil mixing. This low-interference approach encourages the activities of soil organisms, vital for keeping soil productive. It also supports the natural soil state that local plants and their roots have evolved to live in.

IN THE DESERT

In some regions, the parent rock can be very close to the surface. In desert areas, the growing layers are often shallow and a hard layer of a substance called caliche may have accumulated just below the B horizon. Caliche is made of calcium, and cannot be penetrated by plant roots, so desert plants tend to be shallow-rooted.

American agave,
Agave americana

Q Do bonfires harm soils?

SOIL IS AN EXCELLENT INSULATOR and heat rises, so the occasional bonfire seldom does any significant harm to the soil underneath it. And research done into forest fires – bonfires on an infinitely larger scale – reveals that, although the fires destroy organic matter and nutrients in the short term, the soil recovers very quickly provided it is replanted as soon as possible after a fire.

Indirect bonfire damage

Pollution from bonfires is a more indirect form of soil damage, and for this reason there are some things that you should never burn – painted or treated timber, in particular.

Here is why. In the past, paints contained lead, and until recently wood preservatives were based on arsenic, chromium and copper. All of these toxic-heavy metals remain in the ash when burnt, and once in the soil heavy metals remain indefinitely, and can be taken up by fruit and vegetables if the ash contaminates planting sites. Modern wood preservatives often also contain boron, which is also used as a plant food but in

excess can be a potent herbicide. With this number of potential pollutants in play, it is important that all preserved timber be taken to a waste facility – it is simply not worth the risk of burning it.

Even in the absence of pollutants, the ash left by a bonfire is very alkaline and contains useful quantities of potassium, a valuable plant nutrient. When distributed thinly on acid soils, the ash can act as a neutraliser; it is better not left *in situ* at the bonfire site, as it will cause extreme local alkalinity on that particular patch of soil.

A If you always make your bonfire on the same site, however, the soil underneath it will not have the chance to recover fully. Better practice would be either to use an incinerator, or to move the site of the bonfire around so that no single patch of soil bears the brunt.

When soil dries in summer, does it shrink?

THE CHANGING SEASONS subject our soil to constant variations in temperature, and the amount of water flowing both over and through it is also variable. Does this matter? Generally no; soil is very forgiving. But in some cases, when the soil dries out, the resulting shifts demand too much from the buildings erected on it – and it can cause subsidence.

When clay soils dry, they shrink, and cracks appear in the surface. Horticulturally, this is good news: the cracks remain as pores even when the soil gets wet again. Clay soils do a lot to look after their own structure – the fractures resulting from shrinking ensure good drainage and enough air for plants growing in them to develop healthy roots.

The sequence of subsidence

Shrinkable clays shrink in summer and swell in the wetter winters. Buildings on clay rise and fall in summer and winter. When people talk about a building 'settling', this is what they mean. Trees and vegetation can affect this too, since their roots take up water from the soil, causing it to shrink even further. All would be well for the buildings if the clay swelled to its original volume each time it was rehydrated, but it does not.

Most soil is relatively stable: when water is taken from it, it remains at much the same volume. Not all soils are equal, however, and certain clay soils are shrinkable when they dry out.

Each time it rehydrates, it reaches only part of its previous volume. As a result, the foundations of buildings settle lower, year by year.

Buildings with very deep foundations can withstand the vicissitudes of soil shrinkage, but those with relatively shallow 'roots' can suffer structural damage as the soil shrinks away, leaving buildings unsupported, and causing cracks in the walls.

Did the Romans really poison their enemies' fields with salt?

IT'S A POSSIBLY APOCRYPHAL STORY that has long
been accepted as fact – at the end of the bloody Punic
wars fought by the Romans against the Carthaginians,
the victors salted the fields of Carthage so that their
vanquished enemies could not grow crops. But did
that really happen – and, if so, did it work?

Taken with a pinch of salt

The story of the salting of the
Carthaginian fields seems to have
been a 19th-century invention, rather
than one passed down through history.
In Roman times, salt had to be
harvested by manual labour from
saltpans, seawater or brine wells,
rather than being mined mechanically
as it is today, and it was a valued crop
in its own right. Hypothetically
though, if they had salted the fields
thoroughly enough, it would work.
Salt in excess is an effective herbicide
– and a recent study estimated that it

▶ Roman soldiers
were paid in salt or had
provision in their wages
to buy salt, called
salarium, hence our
word for pay: 'salary'.

would take just over 74 tonnes of salt
per hectare to render farming land
completely infertile.

The legend of the salting may have
simply been a way of saying that the
Romans laid the Cathaginian lands
utterly to waste, or, alternatively, the
Romans may have salted the water

◀ In hot regions where
the evaporation exceeds
rainfall, water accumulates
in low-lying areas and
evaporates, ultimately
leading to salty marches,
salt lakes or saltpans.

In ancient times salt was valuable – Roman soldiers were actually given a special allowance for buying it. However much you feared or hated your enemy, you probably would not throw such an expensive resource away.

source that fed the land. This is an effective way to ruin crops: salt is the bane of irrigation, and irrigation systems were already widely used by farmers in the second century BC, the time of the sack of Carthage. If salted water is taken up by plants, it may kill them, and salt will also gradually leach into the ground at root level. Eventually, the irrigated fields will become too salty to grow crops and must either be abandoned for some time or freshly drained to wash the salt out of the soil with plenty of fresh water before they can crop again.

Glasswort, *Salicornia europaea*, a salt-loving plant or halophyte, can tolerate soils too saline for agriculture. Halophytic crop plants would allow use of saline soils.

WHERE SALT KILLS CROPS

Although today irrigation systems in regions with low rainfall are designed from the outset to incorporate excellent drainage – to try to avoid accidental salt accumulation on farming land – they are not always successful. Soil naturally contains a small amount of salt, but much of it is deposited in the water that feeds the crops. By the time it is concentrated enough to become visible (as a white salty crust on the ground), the soil underneath will be infertile. The world's croplands are perpetually on the increase as countries work to feed their growing populations, but, at the same time as land is being cultivated and reclaimed, the total area that is too saline to feed crops is also increasing: in 2014, it was estimated as covering an area the same size as France: 62 million hectares. It is not surprising that there are constant studies ongoing into how to rid the Earth's soil from its natural enemy.

How do worms communicate?

EARTHWORMS ARE NOT KNOWN TO BE GREAT communicators. They do not appear to warn one another of approaching predators, nor do they pass on information about abundant new sources of food. This does not necessarily mean that they cannot communicate – only that studies so far have not gathered much evidence. And the nature of soil – being dark, heavy and opaque – has discouraged extensive research on both worms and other subterranean creatures.

Other experiments seem to suggest that worms may favour herd activity, which, in biology, is often a 'defence in numbers' strategy. Beyond earthworms, recent research

Common earthworm,
Lumbricus terrestris

There are tantalising clues that communication may exist. For example, earthworms seem to be selective when choosing their mates, going so far as to visit the burrows of prospective partners – where it seems unlikely that they would not at least attempt communication.

suggests that the brandling or tiger worms – the long, thin red worms found in compost bins – do show evidence of communication.

By worm standards, nematodes – a family of tiny roundworms that numbers more than 25,000 species, with members that have conquered almost every environment, from desert to ocean – are the master communicators. Experiments at Cornell University revealed that they send chemical signals to each other, but scientists were surprised by the complex form these signals took. The worms could leave chemical

FOLLOW MY LEADER

Various controlled experiments have been done on which senses earthworms use when they are together. In one, worms were released into a maze with food at two different exits. If they were released separately, they went freely to one or other exit; when released at the same time, however, they seemed to favour the same exit. Scientists read the results as showing that worms do not 'tell' each other things by means of chemical secretions (when one worm followed another, but out of sight, it did not seem to be influenced by what the first worm did), but they do exhibit something resembling herd behaviour when they are at close enough quarters to touch one another.

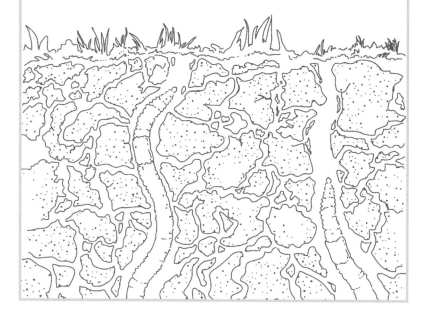

markers in combination – and different combinations had different meanings. For example, the worms might use a pair of chemicals together that appeared to 'tell' worms nearby to go away. But when the same two chemicals had a third added, the signal seemed to tell the other worms to come closer. Even nematodes could not be said to be master communicators, but the sophistication of their chemical language suggests that there may be more to be discovered.

When a plant dies, what happens to its roots?

WHAT HAPPENS ABOVE GROUND WHEN A PLANT DIES
is clear: if it is left undisturbed, it rots and returns to the
soil, the leaves and fleshy parts quite quickly, woody stems
and tree trunks over a much longer period. But what is
happening underground?

When roots rot, they not only supply food for all the organisms underground – fungi, bacteria and wood-boring insects – but they also service the soil: as they disappear, they leave open spaces that aerate the earth and make drainage more efficient. The downside is that they can encourage root-rotting fungi and these do not all limit themselves to dead matter. Some, such as honey fungus or root-rot fungus, are highly efficient and may spread to healthy plants or trees and kill them. For this reason, it is common practice in forestry to grub out the stumps

Roots rot in moist soil, the thin ones disappearing fast, the larger, woody ones sometimes persisting for years. Wood is by nature resistant to rotting, and even the highly adapted – and persistent – bacteria and fungi in the soil take some time to break it down.

and roots of dead or felled trees. Because these can be quite large – about a quarter of the mass of a tree may be in its roots, which could add up to as much as 150 tonnes of stumps and roots per hectare of conifer forest – roots are sometimes actually harvested after tree felling to be used for renewable fuel.

Roots are often overlooked by gardeners, but, when plants die or fail to thrive inspection of the roots often reveals the cause of poorly plants.

What happens if you stop watering?

IN MANY CLIMATES, WATERING IS NOT AS CRUCIAL as a novice horticulturalist might imagine. In the UK at least, in the damp, cool northern and western regions, the soil usually contains enough water for established plants to manage without additional watering. In the driest eastern and southern areas, though, especially where the soil is sandy, most plants will benefit from additional irrigation.

Signs of drought stress can include blueing and waxy leaves, slowed growth and plants that wilt at the hottest time of the day. Unless water shortage is very extreme or prolonged, ornamental plants will recover when rain returns, and brown lawns will become green again, although sustained water shortage can permanently damage water-hungry crops such as tomatoes, *Solanum lycopersicum*, and lettuces, *Lactuca sativa*. In very hot climates with very dry soils, all but long-established and drought-resistant plants will be severely damaged unless watered frequently and regularly.

Plants that have not yet put down a root system established enough to survive periods of dry weather will need extra water. This group includes both seedlings and plants that have been newly moved, even if they are mature.

WATERING WELL

A lot of water goes to waste in gardens, either because the plants did not really need water in the first place, or because water was not used in large enough quantities to make a difference. Briefly wetting plants with the hose does not do much good. Far more effective is thorough but less frequent watering – a soak equivalent to 25mm of rain, given every 10–14 days.

Why do potted plants often fail?

WHETHER THEY ARE KEPT INSIDE OR OUT, potted plants have one key vulnerability: they are dependent on their owner for their survival. Many are killed with kindness by overwatering, while others receive water in random, feast-or-famine bouts that do not meet their needs. And, of course, a few succumb to simple neglect.

When to water

Judging when to water, and how much, is difficult, and there is no simple rule except observation. It helps that overwatering is only actually lethal to a plant if the soil becomes saturated. If the excess water can drain freely, there is much less risk of damage. When drainage is slow – you can see this by how quickly water runs out of the holes in the base of the pot when you water – it is a danger sign: the potting medium is compacting and losing its structure, and there are no longer enough gaps within it to allow the water to pass through and flow out of the pot. Water is retained in the few remaining gaps, and there is no room for air in the pot. Roots cannot function properly without air, and become vulnerable to disease. So if you see slow drainage, repot the plant with fresh potting medium immediately.

House plants are even more vulnerable than potted plants kept outdoors because light levels indoors tend to be low and plants use water comparatively slowly.

Watering house plants

When to water houseplants, then, becomes a matter of fine judgement: the plants need to be allowed to get dry between waterings, but not bone dry. Letting them dry out a little ensures that air has space to enter the root zone. When you water, keep going until the water runs freely out of the pot into the plant's saucer, then allow it to drain. Do not leave the plant sitting in water. If you are feeding your house plants, apply liquid fertiliser in a separate watering, and again wait until it runs through and drains. The plant can then be left until the next watering.

Waterlogging is the number one cause of failure in potted plants. They have much less soil from which to take water than plants in the ground, so need regular and judicious watering that avoids creating either very dry conditions or saturation.

FIVE EASY-GOING INDOOR POTTED PLANTS

Not every house plant is hard to maintain. If you do not have naturally green fingers, here are five that look appealing, but do not suffer from neediness or over-sensitivity. This does not mean that you can entirely neglect them – merely that you can confidently expect pleasing results with minimum maintenance.

Forest or caffre lilies, *Clivia*. These trade long, strap-shaped, deep green leaves and showy, trumpet-shaped, orange, red, yellow or white flowers for moderate amounts of light and reasonable attention to watering.

Dracaena, *Dracaena marginata*. Dracaenas are large and impressive, offering tufty, narrow leaves, in this variety tipped with red. In a friendly spot it can easily reach a height of 2m.

Forest lily,
Clivia

Fiddleleaf fig, *Ficus lyrata*. Large, showy, violin-shaped leaves; can grow impressively large.

Heart-leaved philodendron, *Philodendron hederaceum* var. *oxycardium*. Neat and fast-growing, with trailing, bright green, shiny foliage.

Hens-and-chicks, *Sempervivum tectorum*. The succulent that keeps on giving, producing appealing tight whorls of foliage. Even better, you can take off the 'chicks' to make new plants – and pass them on.

Hens-and-chicks,
Sempervivum tectorum

Dracaena,
Dracaena marginata

Can soils fall sick?

THE HEALTH OF SOIL tends to be judged by the extent to which it can support plant life. A soil may become less healthy for a variety of reasons: it might be sown over and over with the same crops, which depletes it; its structure might be damaged – by building work, for example; or else prolonged flooding or waterlogging might have led to the replacement of beneficial soil life, such as worms, with less useful species that can survive airless conditions, resulting in a corresponding decline in quality.

If a soil is low in nutrients, the easiest way to boost its health and fertility is to add organic material, to 'turn' it by digging or ploughing, which remixes and aerates it, and disrupts the subsoil. Where necessary, drainage should also be improved.

Same site, new crop

Repeated plantings of the same crop on the same site can make soil sick. Certain crops, among them apples, *Malus*, peas, *Pisum sativum*, cherries, *Prunus*, clover, *Trifolium*, and potatoes, *Solanum tuberosum*, are notorious for causing 'sick soil syndrome' (or specific replant disease). While its causes have been established to be biological, not much else is known about them: the probable culprits are fungi, viruses or nematodes.

When sick soil syndrome arises, the grower has three options: to plant a different crop on the plot; to steam-sterilise the soil (which is slow and expensive, but usually successful); or to try biofumigation. For the last, a brassica crop, rich in sulphur-based compounds, is grown on the affected land, then shredded and mixed into the soil; the damaged leaves release a natural chemical called isothiocyanate, which sterilises without significant risk to the environment.

One teaspoon of healthy, fertile soil contains a billion bacteria as well as tens of thousands of fungi, algae and other microscopic organisms.

While a soil may fall sick, it can also recover. The key to a cure, as with human illness, is the correct diagnosis of its condition, followed by the right treatment to encourage it to become well again.

CROP ROTATION

One of the oldest ways of keeping soil healthy is crop rotation. It is very ancient indeed – mentioned by Roman authors – and was well established by medieval times. It is based on the idea that crops have different pests and diseases and take varied levels and mixes of nutrients from the soil, so that rather than grow a crop in the same place, year after year, it is better to grow each crop on a different part of the vegetable garden each year, leaving as long a gap as possible before a crop needs to be repeated. The most usual system today is four-year rotation, so that a crop will return to the same place only every four years – long enough to eliminate any chance of a build-up in crop-specific pest problems or a corresponding depletion in levels of specific nutrients.

Year 1. Potatoes – ideal for breaking up soil

Year 2. Root crops – these leave deep root runs

Year 4. Cabbages require rich soil left by the pea family

Year 3. Legumes and peas need the deep root runs left by the root crops

Does salting soil turn tomatoes salty?

PLANTS THAT HAVE PLENTY OF LIGHT, water and fertiliser often crop heavily. This is good news for farmers, who are paid by the weight or quantity of what they grow, but a lavish yield can mean an equivalent loss in flavour. At some point, everyone has eaten a large, healthy and delicious-looking fruit, a tomato, say, that had hardly any taste at all.

A small amount of stress – perhaps a shortage of water or nutrients – to the parent plant tends to result in smaller fruit but a more concentrated flavour. Watering tomatoes with salty water results in slight stress to the plants – and a better-tasting crop. This theory is supported by research conducted in Israel, where irrigation water that was 10 per cent seawater was successfully used to enhance antioxidants (related to flavour) in crops. Everything in moderation, though. In dry climates or in

Salt, whether ordinary cooking salt or sodium chloride, added to the soil in moderation while the plant is growing will not actually make produce, such as tomatoes, salty, but it can improve flavour.

greenhouses, salt can accumulate to damaging levels in the soil. Outside in a moderate climate, rainfall will flush out surplus salt.

GROW FOR FLAVOUR

You can try the salt experiment on your tomatoes at home, by watering with a salt solution. The time to apply it is after the plants have flowered, at the point when the fruits are just starting to form. Make a strongly salty solution by dissolving 100g salt in 1 litre of water. Add 4ml to a full 9-litre watering can, then water each plant with 2 litres of the solution. Water with this solution weekly (watering with plain water in between times). If your tomato plants start to show signs of leaf scorch, you are overdoing it – flush the surplus salt out with clean water and start again.

Why can't garden soil be used to grow plants in pots?

POTTED PLANTS LEAD A VERY RESTRICTED LIFE. Their root systems are confined, and, if they are indoors or in a greenhouse, they are warmer and so grow faster than their outdoor siblings. The potting medium they grow in must be able to supply a high level of nutrients in a small space, support a rapid growth rate and provide anchorage. It has a demanding job to do.

Plants have not evolved to live happily in pots, so they need a lot of support to do so. It is in their nature to root fairly widely and competitively, and for their root systems to thrive they need water and air. Too much water, though, will kill plants either by drowning the roots or by encouraging disease, and too much air (too many gaps in the potting medium) either makes potted plants susceptible

Garden soil has plenty of virtues, but it is not adapted to the different needs of plants in pots in the way that a specialised potting medium is. It can, however, be modified for use in pots with a few additions.

to drought or imposes an irksome amount of watering on the grower.

Put simply, plants in pots make too many demands on the medium they grow in for garden soil to be able to satisfy them. In fertile, well-managed outdoor garden soils, the opening-up activities of worms and other soil wildlife, plus the availability of much more space to grow in, means that plants can find the right conditions of aeration and moisture for their roots, but, without these outside factors, garden soil is too dense for pots.

MAKING IT WORK

You can modify garden soil to use successfully in pots. Blend two parts soil with one part well-rotted garden compost, then add enough coarse sand to make a crumbly mixture. Add 35g of general fertiliser to each 10-litre bucket of the mix before potting.

Can some plants grow without soil?

GARDENERS ARE ACCUSTOMED TO WORRYING about the pH of the soil in their gardens, and thinking about which soil suits their plants best, how to enrich the soil they are growing in and even how to change the environment of a favourite plant if it does not seem to be thriving. Yet how many remember that many plants in the world do not need any soil at all?

You may well own one of the most popular non-soil plants. The moth orchid, *Phalaenopsis*, the bestselling flowering house plant in the UK, is an epiphyte. If you look into its container, you will not see potting compost but instead a lumpy medium consisting of small blocks of coir or coconut husk, fibrous rockwool and slivers of bark. This mimics the conditions that the orchid would encounter in the wild, where it would grow on tree bark. Their roots are so highly adapted to living on the surface of a tree that

Many plants have evolved to grow without soil, among them: obligate parasites, which damage other plants while growing on them; epiphytes, which grow harmlessly on trees; and lithophytes, which scrape a living on bare rock.

Moth orchids, *Phalaenopsis*, are epiphytes (live on tree branches) but thrive in a pot if a lumpy 'potting media' full of bark chips is used.

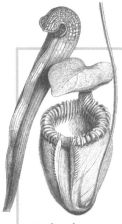

CARNIVOROUS ROCK-DWELLERS

Lithophytes have to scratch a living on bare rock without any access to nutrients. As a result, many have evolved to be carnivores, trapping insects in a variety of ingenious ways, ranging from sticky leaves to the 'pitchers' of the tropical pitcher plants, *Nepenthes*, which first entice insects into containers full of fluid, then ensure they are unable to clamber out again.

Pitcher plant,
Nepenthes villosa

moth orchids can even be grown simply wired to a plain slab of bark, whereas planting them in a conventional potting medium would mean certain death.

Non-soil plants do not always look so much like plants. One of the most picturesque is the Spanish moss, *Tillandsia usneoides*, which is found draping itself from trees in huge swags in the southern states of America. Despite both its name and its appearance, it is not a moss at all but is an improbable member of the bromeliad (pineapple) family. Without soil to draw upon for water, both epiphytes and lithophytes tend to thrive best in very wet environments, such as rainforests.

Other non-soil plants include many aquatic or free-floating species, which need neither the anchorage nor the nutrition they would get from soil. They run no risk of drought, and are adapted to extract nutrients from the water by which they are surrounded. The highly invasive water hyacinth, *Eichhornia crassipes*, falls into this category, as do some more everyday British natives, including duckweed, *Lemna*, and water soldier, *Stratiotes aloides*.

Water hyacinth,
Eichhornia crassipes

Which is the tastiest soil?

WHAT DOES SOIL TASTE OF? And how would you know? Surprisingly, some farmers opt to taste their soil to help them tell how fertile and healthy it is. Fertile soil is reputed to have a sweet taste that is a good match with the smell of healthy, freshly turned earth. Acid soil is said to taste sharp, like lemon juice, and an experienced soil taster can 'read' this acidity and take the hint to raise the lime levels – and thus the pH – of their garden.

Sweet crops from sweet soil

You can take the health of your soil seriously without actually having to eat it. But what kind of care will give you the tastiest and most bountiful crops, whatever you are growing? A sustainable food consultant in Canada conducted a study of different crops grown in different soils when he discovered, back in the 1990s, that how his crops were grown and treated also affected their taste. When he grew

Tasting soil is believed to be a traditional practice that originated in eastern Europe. Practitioners swear that it gives them valuable information about the state of their soil. Soil-borne pathogens can endanger your health, though, so this is not one to try yourself.

Mooli radish is a quick growing and robust cover crop with deep roots that breaks up soil and is under investigation as a soil improver.

cover crops in 'off' seasons he found that the crops he grew on the same land the following season had a sweeter flavour and a deeper, more complex taste. (A cover crop is a crop grown purely to benefit the land it is grown on, and is usually tilled directly back into the soil to give it plenty of extra nutrients.) This was not only an impression he had; it was an improvement that was measurable in Brix units. (A Brix unit measures sugars in liquid. One Brix unit = 1g sucrose in 100g of liquid.) A carrot, say, that had previously registered 8 Brix units would now register 12 units. Not only were the vegetables sweeter, but they also lasted better in storage. His work became the subject of an ongoing study in Canada.

FEED YOUR SOIL WITH COMPOST TEA

Although the science behind home-made compost tea is not fully convincing, many gardeners like to brew this mixture and use it on their soil. If you already have some good-quality, well-rotted compost then it is easy to make your own. All you need is a couple of spades' worth of compost, two large plastic buckets and a large piece of cloth, such as muslin (or an old t-shirt will do) to strain your tea through.

1 Put the compost in one of the buckets. It should be around a third full.

2 Pour in water – ideally from a rainwater butt – up to the top.

3 Leave the mixture to steep for four days, stirring it thoroughly daily.

4 Strain the mixture through the cloth into the second bucket.

5 Dilute the strained mix with more water before use (it should be the colour of weak tea, which usually means that you should use it in about a 1:10 mix – 1 part tea to 10 parts water).

You can use the tea immediately, watered into the soil around plants' roots.

Can soil be made?

THE CLASSIC WAY TO MAKE SOIL takes thousands of years. The millennia-dependent recipe involves many, many years of weathering the parent material – clay, gravel, rock or sand – followed by the gradual accumulation of organic matter and associated soil organisms to complete the process. However, the demand for good soil far outstrips the supply, so can soil be made to meet the need?

How do you make soil?

Typically, an artificial soil starts with a mineral that can be reduced to a satisfactory particle size. Clay is then added to bind the 'soil' together and to help it retain nutrients. The clay is important – it has a tiny particle size with a plate-shaped structure, both of which help it to hold water and nutrients effectively and to release them as plants need them. Next comes the addition of sand and coarse grit, to ensure that the soil will allow water to drain freely, and retain enough air.

Finally, organic matter, often compacted municipal waste – which is both cheap and rich in nutrients – is mixed in, the acidity of the soil adjusted, and fertiliser added if required. Result: brand-new soil – and without the long wait.

Although artificial soils can be made, they are inferior to natural soil in various ways. Even so, they are affordable and effective enough to replace natural soils for many uses, giving at least acceptable results.

OLD-NEW SOIL: A TRADITIONAL RECIPE

Historically, new soil has been created by controlled flooding, a process known as 'warping'. Contained areas of low-level coastal marsh are deliberately flooded with muddy water when the rivers are in spate. Silt builds up in the flooded areas, and the resulting soils are outstandingly fertile. Although it is expensive, the quality results justify the cost.

Clay

Is there soil under the sea?

TRUE SOIL CAN BE MADE ONLY where there is plenty of oxygen, fresh water and specific living organisms to support its structure. Saltwater fosters quite different organisms and biological processes from fresh water, and oxygen is also very limited under the sea. What the sea can offer, however, is plenty of mud and sand.

From sea to soil in 20 years

It is expensive to reclaim land from the sea, but it produces good results. The process, from start to finish, takes about 20 years.

First, the land to be reclaimed is surrounded by raised banking, then the seawater is pumped out, leaving just enough to make it possible for a dredger, a small ship equipped for digging underwater, to excavate a network of drainage channels in the mud.

When the drainage channels have been dug, most of the rest of the water is pumped out, leaving an area of exposed mud under a thin layer of water known as a polder. This is enough encouragement for weeds to establish themselves, and rainfall starts to flush the salt out of the mud. The polder regularly has water pumped out of it until the salt levels have fallen to the point at which reed beds can be sown.

Reed seeds are dropped onto the polder out of a small aircraft flying over it. As reed beds establish themselves, their roots fill the mud-and-sand mix, and salt levels

The sea cannot make soil. However, when land is reclaimed from the sea, it can be made into productive farmland. In some countries, the Netherlands for example, this reclamation has been developed to a very high level.

continue to fall. After about three years, the reed beds are set on fire, and their ashes further fertilise the emerging soil.

Finally, the remains of the reed beds are ploughed into the ground and calcium sulphate in the form of gypsum is added. The gypsum further reduces the salt and encourages the new soil to form small lumps (a process known as flocculation), which makes it more absorbent, accessible to roots, air and rain. At this point it will be able to sustain some crops, and after a further 15 years will be fully fertile farmland.

How long does it take for compost to turn into soil?

IF YOU ARE THE PROUD OWNER OF A COMPOST HEAP or bin, you will be familiar with the 'watched pot never boils' syndrome that affects even the most efficient composter. Some items, even when everyone agrees that they make perfectly acceptable additions to compost, seem to take forever to rot down. So how long should you expect to have to wait before you are forking the black gold onto your vegetable patch?

The perfect balance

The mix of materials is important to the speed they compost: for example, the ratio of green, leafy material to dryer, more straw-like content. If there is a preponderance of nitrogen-rich green material, such as lawn clippings, the mixture may settle into a wet sludge containing so little air that it will take a very long time indeed to rot. On the other hand, if the mix has too much dry, strawlike material, there will not be enough nitrogen to feed the microorganisms that break down the woody parts of the stalks

Composting is a almost like a form of magic; unappetising wastes are turned within a few months into the best soil improver available.

or stems, and it will turn mouldy and – again – rot very slowly. For the speediest results, the best balance is around 30 per cent green material to 70 per cent strawlike, although around 10 per cent more or less either way will not make a huge difference on the clock.

In warm weather, if the compost bin is filled all in one go with a suitable mix of content, 'finished' compost can be ready to use in 8–10 weeks, or as little as six weeks if the bin is emptied and the compost mixed then returned after three. If the bin is filled, as is more usual, with small batches of waste, then the process will take around 12 weeks from the point at which the bin is full – smaller quantities of waste generate less heat. In a cool winter, however, you can expect the process to take at least four months.

Of course, pragmatic gardeners fill their bins as best they can with whatever is available – then forget about them for a year. And their nonchalance is rewarded by very good compost without any worry or fuss.

USE THE KITCHEN TO FEED THE GARDEN

Many kinds of kitchen waste will work well in compost – fruit and vegetable peelings are a staple – although some should be added only in moderation, and a few, such as eggshells, take a fair time to rot down.

- Coffee grounds and tea bags, soft cardboard and newspaper all work well as small additions.

- Citrus peel always used to be thought to be too acid to suit worms, but few now believe this: the only disadvantage to citrus is that unless it is cut into very small pieces it takes ages to rot.

- Do not ever add diseased plant material to the compost, though; burn it on the bonfire, instead.

The rate at which material rots depends to some extent on the season, but there are plenty of other factors that will speed up or slow down progress in the compost heap.

Which animal makes the best manure?

IS MANURE FROM A HORSE BETTER THAN THAT FROM A COW? Are chicken droppings better than ducks'? Many different animals are potential sources of manure for the garden, but is there a *ne plus ultra* when it comes to the best all-round choice?

There are three sorts of farmyard manure. The first is from poultry: chicken, ducks or pigeons. The second is from cows, sheep, horses, donkeys and exotics, such as llamas or alpacas. The third is from pigs. Each has its pros and cons.

Fit for purpose

Poultry manure is rich in nutrients and very fast acting. It is best added to crops in small quantities in spring, but if you use too much it can cause lush leaf growth to the detriment of future flowers, and if there's a real excess it can harm plant roots and cause pollution in the soil. Poultry manure works best if it is composted with plenty of straw, raked-up autumn leaves or other dry materials, before use.

The manure from the animals in the second group – cows, horses and so on – is all quite similar in content: it is low in nutrients, but with high levels of organic material. Again,

Cow manure improves the soil and has useful quantities of nutrients, and is widely and cheaply available in rural areas.

WASTE NOT, WANT NOT?

And what about human manure? Invariably, at some point in any discussion of what works best in the garden, someone will raise the subject of human waste, and almost as predictably quote the fact that, in China, 'night soil' has been used on food crops for generations with impressively fertile effects. Many keen eco-lovers and smallholders are also enthusiasts for the 'waste not, want not' philosophy, but this is one thing that it is best not to try at home. Even though systems exist for composting and processing human waste, there are a number of unresolved hygiene questions that make it a less-than-ideal experiment. If you want to vary the source of your garden manure, consider acquiring a llama.

it is best composted before applying. Horse manure, in particular, tends to contain wood-chip bedding, which may take a long time to rot down in the soil, and which will deplete the nitrogen content of the manure until it is rotted. Other animals are usually bedded in straw, which rots very quickly, so their manure can be applied without the composting stage, if preferred. It is safe to apply large amounts between autumn and spring, and it gives a valuable boost of organic matter to the soil.

The last sort is pig manure. Pigs do not produce such concentrated nutrients as poultry, but most pigs are fed on a diet of grain and soybeans, and this means their manure is more concentrated than that of grazing animals, such as cows or horses, which feed mainly on hay or silage. Pig manure, too, is better composted before being applied to the garden than used fresh, and adds both nutrients and organic matter in a good balance.

Why do some roots grow above the ground?

YOU HAVE PROBABLY SEEN THEM at the base of some trees: humped roots well above ground level. Most tree roots grow quite near the surface in any case – some, such as those of birch, *Betula*, and cherry, *Prunus*, trees, very near – but moving from below the ground to above it is a gradual process that can take many years.

Roots swell and grow over the years and can sometimes emerge above the soil if the soil level falls around them because of compaction, settlement or soil loss.

Much stranger are those species that have developed aerial roots. These include red mangrove, *Rhizophora mangle*, which grow on tropical coasts and elevate themselves on stilt-like legs above the mud where they live. Another swamp dweller, the American swamp cypress, *Taxodium distichum*, puts 'elbows' from its roots above the water, allowing them to breathe.

Strangler trees

Oddest of all is the banyan tree, *Ficus benghalensis*, a member of the Ficus family. It starts life high above the ground as an epiphyte – a plant that grows directly on a host tree. As it grows, it begins to send down long aerial roots around the trunk of its host. These grow and develop, looking as though the banyan is sprouting multiple columns, then eventually fuse together to create a fluted 'trunk' for the new tree. In the process, it gradually smothers its host tree. Although the 'trunk' is actually formed of roots, the 'shoot' part of the tree, high in the sky, continues to send down roots to the ground until they form first a clump and, ultimately, a grove.

In doing this, the banyan avoids the challenge of starting life in the shade of bigger trees or in competition with other emerging plants at ground level. Not for nothing is it nicknamed 'the strangler fig'.

There are a number of reasons why tree roots may emerge from the ground. Sometimes, the water table rises near the surface, encouraging roots upwards; in other cases, the soil becomes so compacted that the roots cannot travel downwards. A few trees, though, have actually evolved to have aerial roots.

Will the world ever run out of soil?

SOIL TENDS TO BE SEEN, mistakenly, as an endlessly renewable resource. But the soils used currently in agriculture were made under natural ecosystems over very long periods. When soil is 'domesticated' in agricultural use, the wild plants and animals that played their part in building it up are replaced by simplified agricultural systems that degrade the soil rather than contribute to it.

Can farmers learn from gardeners?

While farming stands accused of wearing soil out – which ultimately leads to declining harvests – 'gardened' land, used for growing vegetables, consistently scores highly in the soil-quality stakes; that is, aerated soil with plenty of organic matter and nutrients. The key reasons for the sustainability of these garden soils seem to be threefold: the lavish use of organic composts and manures to maintain the levels of organic matter; the wide range of crops that are grown in them; and the fact that the soil is not compacted by being worked when it is wet, or by the use of heavy machinery.

The conclusion? The world will not run out of soil, but we need to be mindful and replace intensive farming methods with gentler, sustainable ones.

Soil damage and erosion are huge problems in the world, even in areas that are not seen as drought- or crisis-prone. Recent research suggests that, even in the UK, the soil in intensively farmed regions has only another hundred harvests left in it unless farming practice changes.

Ploughing is an excellent way to control weeds but damages soil in the long term unless care is taken to restore soil health.

Blood, fish and bone: whose blood, what fish and whose bones?

'BLOOD, FISH AND BONE' is the common – and rather literal – name for a natural combination fertiliser used by almost every gardener as a general feed. It is a slow-release, inexpensive formula that is gentle on plants and offers long-term benefits to the soil. But what is actually in it?

Vegetarians and the squeamish should stop reading now. Blood, fish and bone contains exactly what it says on the tin: it is made from the by-products of food manufacture – the hooves, horns, bones and blood left over when all the parts of animals that humans eat have been used.

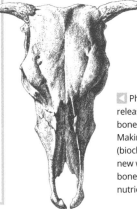

Phosphorus release from ground bones is very slow. Making bone charcoal (biochar) is a potential new way of processing bones to speed up nutrient release.

Waste not, want not

Food manufacture involves processing vast quantities of fish and huge numbers of cows, pigs, sheep and chickens. After the high-end cuts have been removed and some less appealing parts have been used for 'mechanically recovered meat', that amorphous and rather dubious material used for products such as inexpensive sausages and burgers, then the non-edible parts that remain can be turned into fertiliser.

Nutrient balances in the different components of blood, fish and bone vary: fish meal, for example, might contain 10 per cent nitrogen, 6 per cent phosphorus and 2 per cent potassium, while hooves and horns are mostly composed of keratin, a nitrogen-rich, fibrous protein that is slow to break down in the soil. Blood, too, is nitrogen-rich, but releases its nutrients comparatively quickly, and bones are particularly rich in phosphorus, and are finely ground as a fertiliser component.

Although chemically created, nonorganic fertilisers are cheaper and may get a speedier response from the plants they feed. Blood, fish and bone fertiliser is broken down slowly by the microorganisms in the soil, releasing its nutrients gradually across the season as the soil warms up. The rate of decomposition depends on the temperature of the soil, which itself matches the rate of plant growth. The warmer the soil, the faster the plants grow – and the more nutrients released from the blood, fish and bone.

THE MAGIC THREE

The three main nutrients in most fertilisers are nitrogen, phosphorus and potassium. They are often identified on fertiliser packaging by their chemical initials: N for nitrogen, P for phosphorus and K for potassium. The labelling on every fertiliser shows the concentration of each nutrient that it contains.

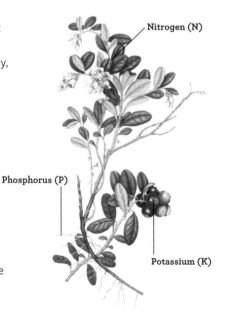

Nitrogen is good for plant growth and gives leaves their characteristic, healthy, deep green colour.

Phosphorus promotes healthy root development and helps the ripening of seeds and fruit.

Potassium is needed for plants to produce flowers and fruits and it encourages plants' resistance to frost damage and fungal diseases.

Nitrogen (N)

Phosphorus (P)

Potassium (K)

How many big animals live in the soil?

APART FROM THE VERY TOP PREDATORS (including humans), animals live a hunted life. And if they cannot run very fast or climb very high, they need to be able to hide when danger threatens. Many animals all over the world dig out shelter in the soil: spaces in which to sit out the winter if you are a bear; dens to use during the breeding season if you are a wolf or a weasel; and, for vulnerable creatures including mice, moles and rats, permanent bases from which to sortie to find food and a mate.

The bigger the animal, the more digging is involved if it wants to carve itself a space out of the soil. And, above or below ground, larger animals need more territory than small ones, so their populations are more thinly spread. Compare the single bear that is found per thousand square kilometres in Finland, for example, with the thousands, sometimes millions, of tiny microbeasts found in every square metre of soil.

More large animals – or large compared with earthworms, anyway – live in the soil than you might think. Generally, the larger the animal, the rarer it is and the fewer you will find per square kilometre of its potential territory.

Small mammals are more populous – more than 24 million rabbits are estimated to live in England, which averages out at around 465 rabbits per square hetare, although the rabbit populations are, of course, grouped, so they are much more concentrated in some areas than others. As the animals get smaller, they tend towards a more even

Brown bear,
Ursus arctos

spread – the commonest mammal in the UK is the field vole, with an estimated population of around 75 million, with the field mouse coming in some way behind at around 38 million. However, populations of all these smaller mammals boom and crash depending on available food supplies – and are, of course, essential food themselves for the predators a little higher up the food chain, such as hawks, owls and weasels.

European or common rabbit,
Oryctolagus cuniculus

HOW LOW CAN YOU GO?

Burrows seldom go deep, as soil is heavy to move and even hibernating animals need oxygen to breathe, so most animals stay comparatively close to the surface. In wet climates in winter, too, the water table may rise high enough to flood deep dugouts. Moles take the idea of subterranean living most seriously, dining off worms and seldom leaving their burrows. Voles, on the other hand, live in the very shallowest runs, just beneath the surface, popping up to snack on plant shoots. Rats also keep to shallow runs, and in extreme danger will dig themselves out and bolt for it.

European mole,
Talpa europaea

Weather, Climate and the Seasons

Is it true that you shouldn't water plants when the sun is out?

THERE IS A LOT OF TRADITIONAL GARDENER'S LORE about the best time to water – and it is often said that you should not water in bright sun. Is this really supported scientifically. Does it matter to plants when you water, so long as they get enough water to keep them happy?

In the past, people believed that water drops on plants' leaves acted as magnifiers, and that sunlight concentrated in spots on the leaves' surfaces caused burnt areas. Recent research casts doubt on this: optical physics doesn't support the theory.

Good timing

Certainly, water on smooth leaves in bright sun does not cause them to suffer. Very hairy leaves may be at slightly more risk: theoretically at least, the water droplets could be held far enough away from the leaf's surface by the hairs to allow light to focus on the surface and, conceivably, cause burning.

However, even if it does not usually scorch leaves, there is another argument against watering in bright sunshine – it can waste water. As much as 18 per cent of output can evaporate as sprinkler drops fly through the air. Watering at night, on the other hand, while it is more economical, can cause other problems: in mild weather, higher humidity and leaves that are left wet in cool temperatures can lead to bacterial or fungal infections in plants. Most experienced gardeners would tell you that the ideal time time to water is just before dawn – and, if that is too early for you to get out the hose or the watering can, a timer-controlled irrigation valve can solve the problem.

Where to water

Ideally, water should be directed at the ground, rather than onto the leaves of plants. Drip or seep irrigation that releases moisture across or sometimes even beneath the soil surface wastes the minimum amount of water even when it is used in full sun. Wetting the root zone is also the most effective way to cool plants down.

HOW TO TELL WHEN A PLANT NEEDS WATERING

If a plant is suffering water shortage to the point at which it is wilting or showing a dull, grey colour in its leaves, the damage has already been done: the plant's growth has stopped, it has become more vulnerable to pests and diseases, and in some cases it may have aborted key parts of its reproductive cycle, such as setting seeds.

To prevent this, you need to be conscientious about checking the soil, particularly when plants are being grown in pots. Soils sometimes look moist when they are not, and vice versa: clay soils, for example, can appear to be wet but the clay particles are so tiny and the water locked so tightly to them that it is unavailable to plant roots. So clay needs to be watered before it shows any signs of drying out. On the other hand, sandy soil may look dry, but, if you pick up a handful, you will find it still feels moist. Although it may not contain a lot of water, what there is, is accessible to roots. With sandy soil, therefore, you need to water only when soil feels dry to the touch.

Wilting leaves

Are roots harmed by freezing?

THE ROOTS OF TENDER PLANTS, such as tomatoes and dahlias, are usually killed outright if they freeze, but many hardy plants can survive frozen roots. Even in moderate climates, such as that in the UK, the soil can occasionally freeze to a depth of 20–30cm, and in cold climates, such as in the American Midwest, the freeze can go much lower, to a depth of as much as 120cm.

Getting ahead in spring

Roots take longer to adjust to the cold, and may never become fully dormant. The process of becoming less sensitive to the cold is gradual, as the roots respond to freeze/thaw cycles as winter sets in. This winter hardiness is then reversed in spring. When the thaw arrives, it is important that plants' roots are ready to leap into action, as early spring is the time when the soil can offer a flush of nutrients, just waiting for plants to take up and use.

When winter arrives and the temperatures start to drop, the parts of perennial plants and trees above the ground enter a state of dormancy and are no longer susceptible to freezing damage. Below the ground, though, it is a different story.

▶ Although older oaks, *Quercus*, lose their leaves in winter, younger ones retain at least some of their leaves.

KEEPING POTS WARM

Unsurprisingly, container-grown plants are especially susceptible to frozen roots. If cold air surrounds the container, the soil inside will reach much lower temperatures than would the root zones of plants grown in the open soil, and, if the air is very cold, the entire root ball may freeze solid. There is no coming back from this, so in cold temperatures it is important to give pots extra protection by wrapping them in bubble wrap or horticultural fleece, or by submerging the whole pot in bark chips.

The roots of evergreen trees, in particular, need to get going quickly in spring. Evergreens keep their foliage, which can be dried and damaged by windy winter weather, so they rely on their roots to undo the desiccating effects of the cold season – and the roots can oblige, provided that they begin to take up water promptly. If they are fast, they can also be first to make use of the water in the soil before deciduous trees, which are rather slower into action, begin to compete for water after their spring 'bud break' – the name for the point at which the leaves of deciduous trees begin to emerge.

Why do some trees drop their leaves in autumn, while others keep them?

IF NATURE WERE LOGICAL, all trees would be evergreen. If you were a tree, surely it would seem irrational to discard all that foliage – massively expensive in energy terms – every year, only to have to grow more when spring comes. Logic suggests that leaves be retained all year, and that they should be large enough to be as efficient at photosynthesis as possible – the larger the leaf, the more efficient it tends to be.

When there are no constraints on growth, trees tend to be evergreen, but with leaves, not needles. They can grow all year and make the best of the conditions available. In wet, frost-free regions where growth is more limited, the trees are often deciduous, and in dry, challenging conditions, whether a hot, dry climate, such as the Mediterranean, or in extreme northerly regions where the soil freezes in winter, needles will serve a tree better, because, although they are not the most efficient at photosynthesis, they are tough. When conditions are too harsh

for evergreen leaves, but not harsh enough for needle-bearing trees, nature has compromised. If the growing season is long enough for there to be time to grow and shed leaves, deciduous trees work well. In regions with a defined winter season, it appears that it is cheaper in energy terms for a tree to grow thin, disposable leaves, shed them when the cold weather arrives and then regrow more in spring.

An area does not have to be all one thing or another. Some natural, undisturbed forest has both conifers and deciduous trees, which share their space and live to their own rules

The answer lies in the climate and conditions in which the tree is growing. In regions with a defined winter season, it is more energy efficient for trees to grow new leaves in spring and shed them in winter. However, this is not a hard and fast rule, as evergreens and deciduous trees can be found growing together.

Bull magnolia,
Magnolia grandiflora

within the same environment. And some broadleaved evergreens find a suitable niche in the understoreys of mainly deciduous forest, where they have good shelter. Holly, *Ilex*, ivy, *Hedera*, and the bull magnolia,

KEEPING YOUR LEAVES ON

Young oaks, *Quercus*, and a few other genera hang onto their spent leaves all winter, and only shed them in spring. This phenomenon is called marcescence. It isn't entirely clear how it benefits the tree, but it may be that the leaves that fall in the spring are more useful to the tree as extra 'food' when they rot on the ground over summer. As the trees mature, they lose the habit and start to drop their leaves in autumn like other deciduous species.

Magnolia grandiflora, are all examples that have evolved to grow under taller trees. They have only a brief period to grow, because, as soon as the foliage of their deciduous neighbours emerges, they fall into shadow and can no longer photosynthesise to any great extent, so they do not have time to shed and regrow foliage every year.

Do plants need watering less when it is humid?

PLANTS ARE AFFECTED BY WATER in the air around them. Water loss from the leaves by transpiration balances up – usually the water passes from the wet interior of the leaf to the drier air around it. However, if there is a high amount of moisture in the air, the leaf will 'leak' less water through its pores.

In most cases of either/or, it is more effective to water a plant's roots than to humidify it. The stomata, or pores, in a plant's leaves close when there is a lack of water, but stay constantly open in humid surroundings, meaning that photosynthesis can proceed unchecked, and a good growth rate will be maintained.

Unfortunately, water vapour diffuses very fast indeed, and wetting greenhouse floors and foliage is seldom fully effective in raising humidity to

The more humid the atmosphere, the less water a plant uses. Humidifying the air (for example, in a greenhouse) can be used as a way of reducing the amount of watering plants need, but it can also increase the risk of bacterial and fungal diseases.

the desired levels. Humidity control by careful ventilation and heating is often needed in greenhouses. Ventilation is the best control as outdoor air is always more humid than the atmosphere in a closed greenhouse. Where ventilation is not possible, as in hot houses for tropical plants where ventilation would allow the heat to escape, water is sprayed into the air as mist or fog, ideally under the control of a humidity sensor.

▼ Humidity control by careful ventilation and heating is often needed in greenhouses. Ventilation is the best control as outdoor air is always more humid than the atmosphere in a closed greenhouse.

TAKING LEAFY CUTTINGS

Humidity is certainly a friend to photosynthesis, and you can take advantage of this when propagating leafy cuttings to ensure they 'take' successfully.

• The cutting should be a short section of shoot 8–12cm long, with some leaves.

• The lower leaves should be removed and the bottom half of the cutting put into a rooting medium (grit and coir mix is ideal). Because the cutting has no roots, it will not at first benefit from watering; instead, the whole environment should be kept very humid, either by covering the pots with plastic lids or by enclosing them in clear plastic bags.

• Cuttings should be kept in the light, but away from bright light or heat (or they will dry out). Humid surroundings and certain amounts of light will ensure they can photosynthesise effectively and will quickly grow roots. As soon as they do, which can be seen when they exhibit some growth in the stem and leaves, they can be judged to have 'taken' and can be watered in the usual way.

The disadvantage with surrounding any growing plant with a very humid atmosphere is that it leaves it vulnerable to diseases, particularly rot. Any browning or damp material should be removed from the shoots as soon as it shows itself.

Why do plants go grey or blue when stressed?

THE GREY OR BLUE COLOURS sometimes seen in leaves that should be green are symptoms of stress in the plant. This may arise from several causes – among them, a period of drought or severe cold, or, in some plants, as a result of a lack of certain nutrients.

A chemical coating

Chemically, waxes are long-chain carbon molecules that are insoluble in water, and making them calls for considerable investment from the plant, through use of its stored sugars, so it will create the wax only when it feels that danger threatens.

The leaf skin, or cuticle, is naturally slightly waxy, but, under drought conditions or other stresses, the wax increases in an attempt to protect the leaves. Such a thickened waxy coating on affected leaves turns them blue-grey.

NUTRIENT-HUNGRY PLANTS

A slightly different blue, within the leaves rather than coating them, can be caused by nutrient deficiencies. Tomato plants, for example, turn blue when they are suffering from a shortage of phosphorus.

In practical terms, the wax not only acts as an impermeable barrier to water loss from the leaf, but also reflects heat and light to help prevent the plant from overheating. When plants are watered, the coating usually quickly thins.

The blue-grey covering is one of many ways that plants protect themselves against stress. They may also send out deeper roots, grow smaller leaves or 'roll' their leaves to reduce their vulnerability. Under drought conditions, the leaf pores will also close to help the plant conserve what water it has.

Can hot soil burn plants?

SOIL IS AN EXCELLENT INSULATOR, so it is unusual for it to get hot enough to burn a plant's roots. If conditions are generally favourable and plants are receiving enough water, their extra seasonal growth in summer will mean that the soil around the roots is shaded by the leaves above it, which will, in turn, help to prevent the ground from becoming too hot.

Where the soil cannot be shaded by foliage, plants have often developed woodier, hairier or waxy leaves. All of these reflect the light rather than absorbing it, helping the plant to avoid overheating.

Making the most of mulches

Plastic sheet mulches are generally used by gardeners to get rid of weeds, but they can affect soil temperatures below the surface, too. White mulches keep soil cool, transparent ones warm the soil, and black ones not only warm the soil but also become very hot themselves, which can cause burnt stems and foliage. Obviously, heating the soil to such a degree is not desirable if you want to maintain healthy roots (or, indeed, living plants), but super-heating can be useful if you want to sterilise the soil. Clear mulches have been recorded in hot regions

If plants are native to the climate they are growing in, they have generally evolved to bear typical temperatures. Heat can affect seed germination, though – we're used to the idea that seeds won't germinate if it's too chilly, but many also won't germinate if they are too hot.

raising the temperature on and just under the surface as high as 76°C, which will kill off life underground and partially sterilise the soil in a process called solarisation.

A more temporary solution to the problem of hot soil in a heatwave is natural mulch, such as bark mulch. Another good material is dry grass as it helps reflect the hot sun.

How do trees know when to drop their leaves?

DECIDUOUS TREES KEEP THEIR LEAVES for the warmer, more temperate part of the year, and shed them for the colder, less favourable, winter season. Evergreen leaves would, in theory, be the most efficient system, but 'proper' evergreen leaves are vulnerable to damage in winter. As a result, most evergreens have converted their foliage to needles – essentially leaves that have evolved to resist weather damage and water loss. They are not as efficient as deciduous leaves, and are only really an advantage to their parent trees in circumstances in which the soil might freeze in winter, making water take-up impossible.

Trees drop their leaves around the same time each year. The primary trigger is the shorter periods of daylight that occur when winter approaches. Falling temperature is an additional factor.

The downside to deciduous

Deciduous trees do need to invest a lot of energy in growing a new set of leaves every spring – and, equally, they discard quite a lot of useful material with their old leaves in autumn. They reclaim as much energy as possible by 'pulling back' all the nutrients as they can into the main tree structure from the leaves before they drop. Falling around the tree's base, the old leaves also rot there and provide some food for the roots in spring.

Leaf fall in specific trees happens at a very similar time each year. The trigger for this is the shorter periods of daylight or more accurately longer nights. The critical period depends on the species and where they grow. Typically, leaf fall is initiated when the days and nights are equal in length. Falling temperature is an additional factor (when the temperature drops, the tree stops producing chlorophyll) but is only an extra. While temperatures can vary a good deal year-to-year, day length is consistent, being the same every year.

How leaf fall works

Light and dark are 'sensed' by phytochrome pigments, which exist in two forms: one made in the light and the other in the dark. As the ratio between the two alters, they initiate changes in the plant hormones that control the different functions in the tree. As the days grow shorter, the tree starts to produce a hormone called abscisic acid, and this causes a corky 'abscission' layer at the base of each leaf stalk. The cells of this layer prevent the flow of nutrients and water into the leaves, and as their supply is cut off the leaves fall.

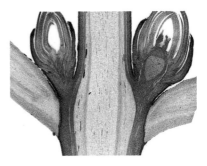

▼ A light micrograph of a vertical section through a sycamore, *Acer pseudoplatanus*, stem node. The red layer at the edge of the stem is the abscission layer, made up of cork and parenchyma tissue (phellogen). It is the first stage of leaf fall in autumn.

LEAF-FALL EXPERIMENTS

Some tests have been carried out in which deciduous trees were kept in growth chambers, spaces in which day length and temperature can be closely controlled. It was found that the trees did not drop their leaves when the temperature was reduced but the 'daylight' hours remained long, but began to shed them when the 'day' length equalised with the length of night. In real life, a similar effect can sometimes be seen when tree branches growing close to street lights remain green and keep their leaves for much longer than trees or branches further away from the light.

How long can a plant survive without water?

AS YOU MIGHT IMAGINE, how long a plant can manage without water depends to a very large extent on the plant. A lettuce seedling would die in a day or two if its roots were allowed to dry out, while some kinds of cacti famously last weeks without water. In one of the most extreme cases, in the superheated, arid conditions of the Atacama desert in Chile, drought-resistant Copiapoa cacti, *Copiapoa echinoides*, possibly the most drought-resistant plants in the world, have been known to live for years without any evident source of water.

Living the dry life

Cacti and other succulent plants are collectively called xerophytes. They have adapted to go without water for days, months or even years. They do not have leaves as such: instead, they have thick, impermeable skin and they may also be covered with thorns or hairs. Their metabolism differs from that of 'normal' plants, too. In most plants, the pores, or stomata, remain open during the day to allow carbon dioxide in so that the plant can photosynthesise. However, perpetually open pores inevitably lead to water loss. Xerophytes, though, close their pores during the hot daylight hours and open them at night, when it is cooler. Because it is dark, the plants

Copiapoa cactus,
Copiapoa echinoides

Some plants have evolved in dry conditions and these can manage well without water for surprisingly long periods, whereas those that been raised with easy access to water will quickly succumb to drought.

cannot press the carbon dioxide into use in photosynthesis straight away; instead, they 'fix' it chemically as an organic acid. When daylight appears the following day, the carbon dioxide is released to allow photosynthesis. The technical name for this system is crassulacean acid metabolism. It is not very efficient – and as a result xerophytes tend to grow very slowly – but it does mean these plants endure in circumstances that would defeat other plants. For gardeners in very hot, dry climates, too, xerophytes are a boon, as they enable the creation of gardens in regions where, without them, any kind of gardening would be impossible.

Echeveria,
Echeveria lurida

WHEN HOUSE PLANTS GO UNWATERED

You would assume that house plants, confined to pots and with limited root space, would be exceptionally vulnerable to water shortage. Many of them, after all, if they are in small pots standing in a sunny position, need watering at least every day and sometimes twice a day. There is a simple way to help them cope with a dry spell, however: if they are grouped together in deep shade, and given a thorough watering, then left, most can last for, say, a two-week holiday period without coming to serious harm. This works because the grouped pots create a humid microclimate, and the shady surroundings ensure that the plants' water needs are kept to a minimum.

Why do some plants survive frost, while others don't?

A SUDDEN AND UNEXPECTED LATE FROST can be devastating to plants. Without a period of increasingly cold temperatures in which to prepare for freezing, it can be fatal. Hardening, the process by which plants ready themselves for tough times, can happen only when temperatures drop gradually, and it is reversible in spring when the harsh weather is past. More worryingly, though, it can also be reversed if there is a mild spell in winter – and if this is followed by a hard frost, the resulting lack of defences can severely damage or even kill a plant.

Hardy plants have two tactics in their repertoire to help them with very cold temperatures. The first is the hardening process, and the second is a process known as supercooling.

How hardening works

The hardening process involves an increase in dissolved sugars and other organic molecules inside the hardening plant's cells. These help to lower the point at which the cells might freeze and prevent ice crystals – which might puncture the cell walls – from forming. The process works like the antifreeze you put in a car, and can stave off ice down to about -2°C. This is a relatively slight protection, so it seems likeliest that the role of the 'anti-freezing' chemicals is also to regulate the rate and location of subsequent freezing in the plant, which will then work in conjunction with supercooling.

Supercooling

Plants 'supercool' when the temperature on several successive days goes down to 5°C. This prompts many hardy plants and trees to prepare for deep cold. Once prepared, their cell contents can go down to temperatures as low as -40°C without freezing solid. This is due to the fact that there are no

Tender plants do not function well at temperatures below 12°C – their cell reactions cease to function. Hardy plants, however, as suggested by their name, can usually survive frosty conditions provided that they are 'warned' by gradually cooling temperatures beforehand.

Willow,
Salix

A TENDER LEGACY

Tender plants have ways of enabling their genes to survive cold conditions, even if the parent plant perishes. Tomatoes, for example, will form seeds that will grow the following year, while potatoes, similarly susceptible to frost, form their tubers as underground storage organs which, again, will grow new plants in the next season. So even though the plant perishes, it has ensured that its progeny live on.

Irish potato,
Solanum tuberosum

small particles or bubbles within the plant's cold sap to act as nuclei for ice crystals, which need nuclei to form. If a hardening period does not take place, supercooling will not happen either.

Even these tactics are not enough in very cold arctic and alpine regions. Birch, *Betula*, and willow, *Salix*, trees in these extreme situations have another process they can call on: they can remove water from their cells and place it between cell walls, where it freezes harmlessly. Most plant cells die when they are dehydrated, but in this case evolution has enabled them to manage: there seems to be no practical limit to the degree of cold that the dehydrated cells can survive.

How do bulbs know when to come up?

BULBS, OR GEOPHYTES TO USE THE BOTANICAL TERM, typically come from regions where plants need strategies to shelter from difficult climate conditions. And where better to stay relatively safe from freezing cold, burning heat or hungry herbivores than underground? Growers know that, within certain limits, spring bulbs (and corms and tubers, too) flower at much the same time every year, suggesting that a sophisticated control mechanism is at work.

Temperature dictates when bulbs emerge from the ground, and many seem to need a cold snap before they begin to grow. The mechanics behind this are not entirely understood, but clearly at some level bulbs have both a 'clock' and a 'thermometer' that tell them when it is safe to start growing.

Daffodil,
Narcissus

Spring-flowering bulbs come from regions with very hot summers and cold winters: Mediterranean climates at higher altitudes, where daffodils, *Narcissus*, snowdrops, *Galanthus*, and cyclamen, *Cyclamen*, originate, and semi-arid regions with dry winters and summers, where ornamental onions, *Allium*, tulips, *Tulipa*, and some irises, *Iris*, come from, are classic examples. Bluebells,

Tulip bulbs

Hyacinthoides, have evolved to make use of the brief period of good light between the end of winter and full leaf cover on trees.

How flowering happens

Temperature is the bulbs' trigger. Bulbs need a set period of cold, but not freezing, weather, ideally around 5°C, before they can form their flowering spike. It is believed that this affects the levels in the plant of gibberellins and auxins, hormones that stimulate plant growth. In tulips, the flower begins to develop in hot soil in late summer, but will begin to grow only in the following spring after a period of cold (in grower's terms, the cold 'releases' the bulb from inhibition, and sparks growth). Some other bulbs, such as lilies, *Lilium*, won't even begin to form their flowers until after their cold period (the technical term for this is vernalisation). They have to develop their flowers from a standing start, which may be why they flower later than tulips. But whichever pattern they follow, cold is an important factor in the bulbs' development.

WINTER- AND SUMMER-FLOWERING BULBS

Bulbs that flower in winter and summer do not call for such precise temperatures. Jonquil bulbs, for example, the group that contains the popular, delicate *Narcissus* 'Paperwhite', which is often very early in the garden, will, if it is warm enough, flower in both autumn and winter, without needing the prompt of a cold snap. And summer-flowering bulbs, such as freesias, *Freesia*, and gladiolus, *Gladiolus*, simply flower when the plant has had enough time photosynthesising to get together sufficient resources to bloom.

Freesia,
Freesia caryophyllacea

What are rain shadows?

WHEN AN AREA IS PROTECTED FROM RAINFALL by hills or mountains that stand in the path of prevailing rain-bearing winds, it is called a rain shadow. In hot regions, when the mountains blocking the winds are also high, the combination may result in an area of desert. Death Valley, which lies in the rain shadow of the Sierra Nevada mountains in California, is a classic example of this sort of extreme climate, with an average annual rainfall of just 6cm.

A rain shadow is an area protected from rainfall by hills or mountains. In certain climates, a rain shadow can act as a helpful moderator. In very wet regions, the warmer, drier conditions fostered by rain shadows may be welcome to the gardener.

Within the UK, Wales offers another rain shadow example – and one much more friendly to horticulture. Along its western edges, Wales is very wet indeed, and grows excellent camellias, hydrangeas, magnolias and rhododendrons, but many other plants do not appreciate the near-constant moisture: Snowdonia, in north Wales, has an annual average rainfall of almost 4.5m – not enjoyable for anybody except ducks. Move to the lee of the Welsh hills, into the vale of Evesham, though, and the climate grows much warmer and drier – giving the cider, fruit- and vegetable-growing industries a boost.

The lesson? If you are a gardener and you are researching a new location, do not just check out which way the garden faces; check out the local microclimate too.

◀ Camellia, *Camellia sasanqua*, thrives in wet regions, but would not do so well in a rain shadow area.

How much water does a tree use in a day?

LIKE ALL PLANTS, trees do not need much water for their internal processes. The vast majority of the water they take up from the ground is used for transpiration – the loss of water vapour through the tree's leaves that is a key part of photosynthesis. How much water the tree needs daily depends on a number of factors.

Location and weather dictate how much water a tree requires. The warmer, drier and faster-moving the air around it, the more water the tree will need. A tree in a forest, or in an urban setting surrounded by buildings, will drink less than a solitary tree exposed to constant wind.

DO TREES DRINK MORE THAN GRASS?

You might think that a tree would need more water than a lawn, but all vegetation growing in moist soil actually transpires much the same amount of water.

Heavy drinkers

It is difficult to generalise – tree requirements vary so much – but, on average, a large tree can take up more than 450 litres of water from the ground in a single day, making it a very thirsty organism indeed. It will use most of this in transpiration, evaporating water through its leaves. Even in regions where there is regular and heavy rainfall, there may not always be enough water in the soil to maintain a supply at this rate. In woods and forests, much of the rain that falls is intercepted by the canopy of greenery far above the ground and evaporates straight back into the atmosphere. When trees cannot fulfil their water requirement, they are able to close the stomata, or pores, in their leaves in order to slow down transpiration and thus water loss.

Why does frost make some vegetables taste better?

IN THE PAST, KEEN VEGETABLE GARDENERS often would not harvest their winter root crops until there had been several hard frosts. They knew that, if harvested before a frost, vegetables such as parsnips might have a chewy, starchy taste, whereas after a frost this would have transformed into a much sweeter, more palatable flavour – although they may not have known why.

The science behind the sugar

From the vegetable's point of view, converting some of its starch to sugar makes sense in cold weather because the sugar helps to prevent the water in its cells from freezing. The sugar molecules mix with the cooling water in the vegetable, and this stops the water molecules rising and freezing: in effect, they lower the freezing point of the vegetable. So the water in a parsnip, say, might be freezing cold – but it still will not turn to ice.

Vegetables often store most of their winter food reserves in the form of starch; in cold weather, this breaks down to produce sugars: hence the improved flavour of the crop.

This extra sweetness occurs in both root and green vegetables. The technical reasons are not always the same: in Brussels sprouts, *Brassica oleracea*, for example, the sweeter flavour is thought to be because cold weather reduces the bitter compounds that are present in the crop, rather than because of a starch/sugar conversion.

Not all winter vegetables are frost-hardy, though, and many, such as beetroot, carrots and turnips, need to be protected by covering with a layer of straw when temperatures drop very low.

DO NOT LET POTATOES FREEZE!

Unlike many other crops, potatoes, *Solanum tuberosum*, are not improved by frost. The flesh turns brown and, when cooked, they have an almost caramelised flavour that is not good. Protect your potato crop from very low temperatures.

VEGETABLES THAT TASTE BETTER IN WINTER

Not only do all these vegetables taste good, but every one offers substantial health benefits, too.

Cabbage. Most types will withstand very low temperatures without coming to any harm, the cold only serving to enhance their flavour. Healthwise, cabbage is rich in vitamins A, B and C, along with anti-inflammatory micronutrients, or polyphenols.

Collard greens

Collard greens and mustard greens. Two types of easily grown winter greens, both of which are rich in vitamins A and K1 and antioxidants.

Mustard greens

Kale. One of an ever-increasing number of 'superfoods', kale does more than most to earn the label, with plenty of vitamins K1, A and C, antioxidants, plus all nine of the amino acids that make protein in the human body.

Kohlrabi

Kohlrabi. A vegetable that grows rapidly even in very cold temperatures, guaranteeing a quick crop. It has high levels of glucosinolates, natural compounds that have been credited with antibacterial and anti-parasitic properties.

Parsnips. Easy to boil or roast, with a nutty, sweet flavour, particularly rich in potassium, fibre and vitamin C.

How do plants stay alive in the desert?

ALTHOUGH WE TEND TO USE THE WORD 'DESERT' as a catch-all for any hot and barren place, true deserts are actually extremely various, ranging from barren wildernesses of sand and rock where rain may fall only once in a decade to comparatively fertile regions with predictable, if sparse, rainfall, and relatively moderate temperatures. And plants, being the adaptable opportunists that they are, have found their place in most deserts by evolving to cope in their surroundings.

Plant life in some form exists in most deserts, though a few are challenging for even the most flexible plants. Different species have developed all kinds of methods for dealing with exceptionally hot and dry conditions.

Five deserts

Just how different deserts can be is illustrated by these five examples.

Atacama Desert, Chile

Exceptionally dry and barren, with an average annual rainfall of just 1mm, although in many years no rain falls at all. Even plants find these conditions a challenge, with just a few cacti managing to scrape a living on the desert's hills, where things are a little cooler and damper.

Karoo Desert, South Africa

A high desert, with an altitude of up to 1,000m, moderate temperatures, and a predictable winter rainfall of up to 20cm. Plants grow and set seed quickly in spring, leaving their seeds dormant through summer and winter, to sprout and flower equally quickly the following spring.

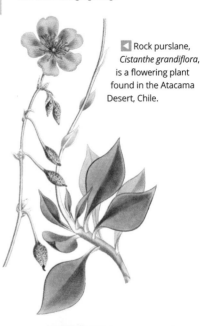

◄ Rock purslane, *Cistanthe grandiflora*, is a flowering plant found in the Atacama Desert, Chile.

🔺 The tree tumbo, *Welwitschia mirabilis*, is a bizarre shrublike plant of the Namib. It continuously grows two long strap-shaped leaves, which can grow several metres long.

more different plant species in this desert than in any other, and they grow relatively large. In particular are the resin-rich creosote bush, *Larrea tridentata*, (which smells strongly of its namesake) and the saguaro cactus, *Carnegiea gigantea*, which has shallow, wide roots adapted to using even the lightest shower of rain.

Namib Desert, Southern Africa

A coastal desert, with just 10cm rain annually. The plants that manage here depend on coastal fog condensation and seasonal water courses for moisture.

Sonoran Desert, North America

This desert has a relatively wet climate with 8–40cm of rain falling annually in two 'wet' seasons, one in summer and one in winter. There are

Thar Desert, between India and Pakistan

Unusually, the Thar Desert is highly populated. It has a monsoon rainfall, with 10–50cm of rain falling during the late summer months of the monsoon season. Its commonest plant is the khajri tree, *Prosopis cineraria*, which has roots that grow unusually deep and an unusual tolerance for the salty water that it finds deep underground.

FIVE WAYS THAT PLANTS COPE IN THE DESERT

The survival strategies of desert plants include:

• The ability to absorb a lot of moisture quickly.

• A waxy coating to keep the moisture in.

• Defence strategies, such as the prickles on cacti, that discourage equally moisture-hungry animals from eating them.

• A water-conserving form of photosynthesis, which means the plant's pores open only at night.

• An ability to become dormant during exceptionally punishing seasons, and to spring to life again when the weather improves.

How does grass survive under snow?

IN VERY COLD WEATHER, turf grass often turns brown – the leaves are either killed by the temperature or dried out by the wind, and the soil is frozen, so the plants' roots cannot replace the water lost. Though they may dismay gardeners, brown lawns will recover: the active growing area is at the base of each grass blade, and will regrow as soon as it gets the opportunity.

Snow may actually offer protection to turf grass, and, if it is not very deep, allows some light through to the plants so that they can photosynthesise. Grass will usually survive even under deep snow, provided that both the cold and the thaw are gradual rather than sudden.

The pros...

Snow offers insulation and moderates sudden temperature shifts. Otherwise, if temperatures rise and then suddenly fall again, for example, when there is a cold snap after a period of thaw, it can be extremely damaging to any plant.

Fallen, uncompacted snow also contains plenty of air, so grass does not 'drown' under snow as it would if it were waterlogged, although snow-covered grass will not actually grow, since the temperatures are too low – the trigger for growth acts only when the thermometer rises above about 4°C.

What is it that makes grass hardy? Like some other plants, turf grasses contain their own antifreeze in the form of sugars inside their cells. The sugars mix with the cooling water and interfere with the formation of ice crystals. Frozen water swells and would burst the plants' cells, so the sugars are a life-saver for the grass.

And the cons...

Despite its protective qualities, snow could not be said to be actively good for grass. Carbon dioxide levels can increase under the snow layer, which can, in turn, increase fungal activity and leave grass more susceptible to disease. When it melts, the slush from melting snow can leave the grass less hardy. Farmers know this very well: many hay fields, for example, are located on a slight slope to make sure that heavy excess water is carried away and does not damage the grass crop.

There is also a phenomenon called snow moulds, in which patches of dead or yellowing grass appear after snow and spread until drier, warmer weather conditions arrive and promote new, healthy growth. This is caused by two specific and sonorously named fungi, *Typhula incarnata* and *Monographella nivalis*, both of which are opportunists that take advantage of the grass's weakened state.

DORMANT SEEDING

In cold areas, some gardeners 'refresh' their lawns or replace bald patches by sowing grass seed in late autumn just before snow. This is called dormant seeding and is said to work because it allows the seed to take immediate benefit from the damp, warm conditions as the snow thaws and to germinate before local birds can start snacking.

Why do leaves change colour in autumn?

As WINTER APPROACHES, signalled by shortening days and falling temperatures, trees take measures to conserve their energy. Nutrients that were held in the leaves, especially chlorophyll, are broken down and sent back into the trunk and roots to be kept out of harm's way during the winter. Unwanted materials that the tree has taken up, on the other hand, such as silicon and metal traces, are transferred into the leaves and shed with them when they fall.

The recipe for autumn colour

When the chlorophyll travels back across from the leaves into the trunk and roots of the tree, the other pigments come into play, turning the foliage the rich colours characteristic of autumn. Carotenes and xanthephylls create yellow, while reds and purples come from a mix of anthocyanins plus any sugars that are lingering in the leaf. Remnants of chlorophyll combined with

Maples, *Acer*, often have spectacular autumn colours.

anthocyanin work with warmth and light to produce brilliant shades, which is why the cold or overcast autumns common in Atlantic Europe are less effective at generating colour than the warm, bright Indian summers more prevalent in New England, where the fall colours are famously vivid.

ALeaves are green because the main pigment in them is chlorophyll. In winter, one of the ways in which trees conserve energy is by pulling chlorophyll and other nutrients back into the trunk.

CATERPILLAR CAMOUFLAGE

Autumn can be bad news for caterpillars. Many have devised ingenious camouflage to blend in with the summer foliage of their host plants, and some, such as the caterpillar of the American peppered moth, *Biston betularia cognataria*, can adapt their camouflage to blend in with more than one host. This particular caterpillar can match itself to no fewer than 13 different host trees. Even more impressively, while some caterpillars achieve their colour changes by eating a certain diet, the peppered moth caterpillar needs only to see a colour in its host to match it.

However, in autumn this changes. For some reason, it appears that caterpillars are unable to mimic the bright colours of the turning leaves. And as their camouflage fails, the caterpillars stand out clearly to predatory insects and birds. Some have a secondary protection – either by tasting bad and advertising the fact with loud colouring, or by coming out to feed at night when fewer predators are about. But the wise caterpillar gets on with spinning its cocoon when autumn comes.

Peppered moth, *Biston betularia*, caterpillars on birch, *Betula*, (left) and willow, *Salix* (right)

Why don't plants flower in winter?

IF YOU ARE ASKED TO NAME YOUR favourite flowers, the vast majority that come to mind will be those that are around in the spring and summer. But if you think a bit harder, you will find that you are also able to name quite a few – hellebores, *Helleborus*, snowdrops, *Galanthus*, winter honeysuckle, *Lonicera* – that flower in winter, when they are far more noticeable in an otherwise rather empty garden.

Winter versus summer flowering: pros and cons

There are evident advantages to flowering in winter for some species. Wind-pollinated plants take advantage of both the breezy winter weather and the absence of deciduous foliage that might intercept airborne pollen before it can reach female flowers.

For plants that rely on pollination by insect, winter flowering may be a way to avoid competition. If they flowered in summer, they would have to invest significant resources in scent and colour to produce flowers with the appeal to compete with all the others in bloom. And while summer-flowering plants may call for specific pollinators, those that flower in winter cannot afford to be fussy – pollination must be feasible by any passing insect, be it bee, beetle or fly. Winter-flowering plants have to ripen their seeds in the cooler, duller conditions of spring, but this can give them an edge in germination, as they can seize any good growing spots early in the season, before the later seed-setting of the spring- and summer-flowering plants.

Snowdrops, *Galanthus*, flower from autumn until early spring. Each species has a defined flowering period.

Although we think of flowers being a spring and summer phenomenon, a number of plants actually do flower in winter. They do so for a number of reasons.

How long could a tree survive in the dark?

WE CHOOSE AND EAT OUR FOOD from external sources, but a tree must make its own by means of photosynthesis, and this depends on both light and water. Photosynthesis cannot take place in the dark, although respiration must go on, or the tree would die. And, of course, the tree will eventually die without food, but the process will be slower.

Hungry or thirsty?

We all know that an animal would die of thirst long before it died of hunger, and plants are the same. Water is the immediate need, while food is a necessity in the longer term. If you placed a deciduous tree in the dark (and this is hypothetical, because, as far as we know, no experiments have been done on the subject), it would send its nutrient resources to its roots and quickly shed its foliage, just as if it was entering its semi-dormant state in winter. The upper part of the tree, mostly hard timber that is not living but is covered by a living skin of water and nutrient-conducting cells, would have a very low requirement for nutrients in the dark.

With its top in a dormant state, the tree would rely on its roots to survive. If the tree's surroundings, as well as being dark, were also cold, root activity would also be reduced and the potential survival time of the tree would increase. Large trees do have commensurately large nutrient stores,

A tree kept in the dark cannot make food, so it will eventually starve to death. How long that will take will depend on what sugar stores it has, and the ready availability of water.

which might enable them to survive some years, even without the possibility of photosynthesis, but, without the means to make more food, they would eventually succumb to starvation.

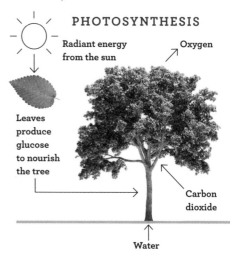

PHOTOSYNTHESIS

Radiant energy from the sun

Oxygen

Leaves produce glucose to nourish the tree

Carbon dioxide

Water

What happens to the frogs in the pond if it freezes?

IN THE UK, FROGS ARE NATIVES, well-adapted to the climate and with an important role to play in gardens – feeding on insects and helping to control garden pests in the process, while making an appealing menu item themselves for birds and snakes. Open ponds in the countryside are becoming increasingly rare, so garden ponds make valuable homes for frogs – but how do they manage in a cold winter?

A frog's life

The common frog, *Rana temporaria*, is the species most usually found in the UK. In winter, their metabolism will slow down, enabling them to conserve energy, but they still need some oxygen and may also swim around in milder periods. Their survival depends on the pond being deep enough – if the pond is 45cm or more deep, an average freeze will not reach the mud at the bottom and thus will not affect the frogs. If a small, shallow pond does freeze over, the ice may prevent oxygen from dissolving in the water, and could possibly lead to

Frogs sometimes overwinter on land, hibernating in piles of logs, small gaps in rocks or heaps of dead leaf litter. When they do spend winter in the water, they stay around the muddy layer at the bottom of the pond, where there is still oxygen to be had.

▶ The common frog, *Rana temporaria*, is found in the UK and widely across Europe. It is able to slow down its metabolism in winter in order to conserve energy.

OVER THE POND

In less temperate regions, frogs can have much more to deal with. In some parts of America where really fierce winters are the norm, some terrestrial frog species, such as the wood frog, *Rana sylvatica*, find a quiet corner to overwinter, freeze and then thaw out, none the worse, in spring. This would not be possible for most living things. There are high water levels in every animal's cells and when water freezes it expands, so the cells would burst. Wood frogs, though, have evolved to cope; not only are their cell walls especially elastic, with enough 'give' to withstand freezing, but also the cells of their key organs, deep inside their bodies, contain unusually high levels of glucose, which prevents them from freezing at all. A wood frog in midwinter may appear to be completely frozen – it will not be breathing, or have a heartbeat – but in spring it will thaw and miraculously come to life again.

Wood frog,
Rana sylvatica

suffocation for frogs living at the bottom, but, in deeper or wider ponds, this is unlikely. If you have a pond and you worry about your frogs' welfare during a prolonged cold spell, use a pan of hot water to melt a hole in the iced-over surface once or twice a week. This may ensure that enough oxygen can dissolve in the cold water to meet the frogs' quite modest requirements.

▼ The northern leopard frog, *Lithobates pipiens*, survives the severe winters of Canada and the USA by hibernating at the bottom of ponds and streams.

Chapter 5

In the Garden

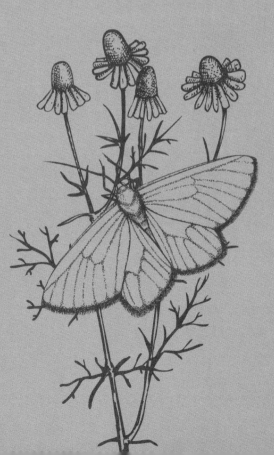

How do you keep spiders out of a shed?

UNLESS YOU ARE ONE OF THE FOUR PER CENT of the population who suffers from arachnophobia, the best tactic may be to learn to share your space with spiders. They are wonderful predators who have a valued place in the food chain, both suppressing a whole range of pests and providing food for birds and other wildlife.

If you feel strongly enough about it, not even spiders can get into a space that has been sealed hermetically with silicone mastic. But it seems rather unfeeling to deny winter accommodation to some very useful members of society.

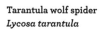

Tarantula wolf spider
Lycosa tarantula

Even if you are not afraid of spiders, in autumn, when their breeding cycle peaks, you may find them rather too much of a good thing. As temperatures drop, they come indoors, and sheds, which usually have more gaps than well-insulated houses, may become particularly overrun. If you do not want to spend a lot of time in the shed waving tubes of mastic about, consider these traditional repellents.

Folklore holds that spiders cannot stand the smell of either conkers or walnuts. So lay out a bowl of either or both – it is worth a try. Even more fancifully, it is claimed that spiders move away from the colours blue, so you could give the shed a sky-blue facelift. Possibly with more basis in fact, strongly scented oils, such as citronella or peppermint, are also believed to deter spiders. Again, there is no hard scientific evidence, but you could try them and see.

Finally, console yourself (if you are not reading this in Australia, that is) with the fact that the majority of British spiders are harmless to humans. In Australia, venomous spider bites are quite frequent and do serious damage. Down Under, you really would do well to insulate your shed.

When does a bed become a border?

MOST PEOPLE'S IDEA OF A CULTIVATED GARDEN features flower beds: even the Hanging Gardens of Babylon were said to have featured 'plants grouped together in fine array' and beds were already playing an important part in gardens by the time the rich villa owners of Ancient Rome were taking pride in their planting. Garden beds have also proved fairly resistant to the vicissitudes of fashion: they are just as popular in gardens today.

A bed is simply any plot of land that is used for the cultivation of plants, while a border is, as its name suggests, a long bed that is arranged along the edges of something, whether it is a wall, a path or a fence.

While beds in modern gardens are often fairly fluid in form, in the 17th and 18th centuries they were usually part of a parterre, a formal arrangement of sometimes elaborately shaped beds in a broadly symmetrical pattern. Since the beginning of the 20th century, the style has been less set, with island beds sitting in lawn or amongst paths. The traditional form for a border has been long, typically backed by a wall or hedge, and ideally deep, too, the better to show off various heights of a colourful mix of herbaceous annuals and perennials. The length record for a border is set by examples at Dirleton Castle in Scotland, which measure up at an impressive 215m.

PRAIRIE PLANTING

Beds show no signs of going out of style, but planting habits do change. Increasingly, beds and borders are being planted with self-sustaining communities of plants that do not need a heavy-labour timetable of weeding, feeding, staking and splitting. Prairie plantings that mimic naturally flower-rich grasslands are currently very popular. They need to be cut back hard in spring but are otherwise admirably low-maintenance.

Who invented the garden gnome?

LOVE THEM OR LOATHE THEM, these kitsch little characters have deep historical roots. A liking for whimsical and often strikingly smutty garden sculptures goes as far back as Roman times. By the 17th century, the fashion had travelled to Germany, but it was only in the 18th and 19th centuries that the figures became recognisable as the garden gnomes we are familiar with today.

From the Black Forest to British suburbia

German gnomes had many links to the folklore of the Black Forest, and it is probably thanks to this that they were frequently depicted as miners, often carrying picks and spades. As tourism to the Black Forest grew through the 19th century, the figures began to return home with visitors as souvenirs, and garden owners started to collect them. Gnomes dating from this period are now sought-after antiques with quite high price tags, although the fashion for importing them died out with the First World War and the resulting anti-German sentiment.

Gradually, the fashion trickled down, until gnomes became regular adornments in quite modest British gardens, and workshops were set up to manufacture them in weatherproof cement. Their heyday was in the 1950s and '60s, when they offered an outlet for the creativity of their owners, who often set them out in arranged tableaux, indifferent to snobbish

The first gnomes that resemble today's examples were made in Germany and, perhaps surprisingly, were high-status objects made from carefully cast and painted terracotta or even porcelain. They were also rather larger than their modern brethren, at around 1m high.

accusations of bad taste. And keen collectors still exist: in 2012, the Gnome Reserve in Devon had 2,042 on show, just pipping a Lincolnshire collector who, at the time of his death in 2015, owned more than 1,800 'little people'. While the 'straight' use of gnomes is probably on the wane, they are still popular ironic ornaments in many gardens.

▲ Gnome kidnapping and holding them for ransom are modern tongue-in-cheek crimes.

ARISTOCRATIC FOREBEARS

There is a story that today's jolly, pint-sized, affordable British gnomes are direct descendants of a collection of German terracotta figures imported in the 1840s by Sir Charles Isham, owner of Lamport Hall in Northamptonshire, where they were put on display in a specially constructed rock garden, the better to show off their charms. (The rock garden is still open to visitors, but only one of the original gnomes, known as Lampy, survives.) These aristocratic origins have done nothing to endear their descendants to RHS Chelsea Flower Show, which has exercised a ban on gnomes throughout its hundred-year history – a ban that was briefly lifted in 2013, but swiftly reimposed the following year.

Why do slugs eat some plants and not others?

WHAT IS IT THAT PLACES SOME PLANTS firmly on the menu for slugs, while others go untouched? Is there a list of qualities that leaves have to meet, or do slugs have varying palates according to, say, the weather or the time of year? And, finally, most importantly of all, is there any such thing as a slug-free garden plant?

Slugs enjoy a wide range of garden plants, but top of their list are young, succulent, soft, nutrient-rich leaves, which are not yet old enough to have become leathery or to have developed any chemical defences.

some varieties have higher concentrations of toxic chemicals called alkaloids in their skin than others (most have them to some degree), and these suffer far less slug damage than those with a lower concentration. Generally, too, slugs do not favour very hairy or coarse-textured leaves if there is anything softer to munch on.

Apart from inbuilt chemical defences, birds are the greatest natural predator of slugs, so if they are encouraged into the garden with extra food and water, they will return the favour and reduce the slug population while they are there.

Fighting the slug war

Often a gardener's most highly prized seedlings fit neatly into the 'slugs' favourites' category. Some plants have ways of developing their own defences, but there are ways that you can help them repel the slimy predators, too. Many plants use chemicals to make themselves distasteful to slugs. This is known as chemical ecology, but it does not usually kick in until plants have moved beyond the seedling stage. One example is found in potatoes:

The gardener can avoid young plants becoming slug food by raising them in pots, which can be easily defended, in a 'safe' area of the garden (perhaps by placing them on a small area of sharp sand, or in a greenhouse), and only planting them out when they are big enough to withstand slug grazing.

Finally, natural inhibitors can be watered onto foliage – solutions of garlic or of calcium chloride are both effective. Calcium chloride is exceptionally bitter, and slugs do not seem to care for garlic, either. Unlike the chemicals naturally produced by plants, though, these watered-on mixes will wash off in rain and will need to be reapplied.

TEN PLANTS SLUGS LOVE – AND TEN THEY HATE

It is worth taking note of this before you plan your garden – you can save the heartache of seeing slugs chomp up all your favourites by planning ahead.

Slugs love:

- Celery
- Plantain lillies, *Hosta*
- Lettuce
- Petunias, *Petunia*
- Runner beans
- Tulips, *Tulipa*
- Dahlias, *Dahlia*
- Delphiniums, *Delphinium*
- Gerberas, *Gerbera*
- Peas

Slugs hate:

- Bear's breeches, *Acanthus mollis*
- Lady's mantle, *Alchemilla mollis*
- Elephant's ears, *Bergenia*
- Bleeding heart, *Dicentra spectabilis*
- Foxgloves, *Digitalis*
- Fuchsias, *Fuchsia*
- Pelargoniums, *Pelargonium*
- London pride, *Saxifraga x urbium*
- Nasturtiums, *Tropaeolum*
- Verbascums, *Verbascum*

Plantain lily, *Hosta*

What food makes the best compost?

THIS MAY NOT BE A QUESTION YOU OFTEN CONSIDER since, by definition, the human food that ends up in your compost consists of leftovers – no one would buy food purely to benefit their compost bin.

Even the more compost-friendly end of the human diet – vegetable peelings – can be too nitrogen-rich to be helpful if included in quantity, and will need to be mixed with plenty of drier, strawlike material to get a balanced, crumbly-rather-than-wet compost.

Other ways to compost

If you do not want to risk sacrificing the balance of your 'main' compost bin, there are alternative ways to ensure that your leftovers do not go, well, to waste. Small-scale bins specifically for food remains are available and,

although they do not result in much compost, what they produce can be of high quality. They consist of solid, rat- and mouse-proof bins with mesh floors: air circulates freely inside them and the rotting process is quick and – because anaerobic, or airless, decomposition is not happening – relatively smell-free. Any liquid waste falls through the mesh onto the ground underneath where it will be dealt with by the bacteria in the soil.

If you are not keen on having a compost bucket forever present in the kitchen, using a Bokashi composter ensures that you can actually make a small quantity of food-waste compost indoors without either seeing or smelling it. Bokashi compost bins are sealed and 'fed' with carefully selected microbes and fungi to break down waste food efficiently and quickly.

◀ In harder times, people would peel spuds and plant the peel. The peel retains 'eyes' (buds) that will grow then into new plants.

Q Is pee good for plants?

MANY ORGANIC GARDENERS who like to see sustainability through to its logical conclusion water their gardens with dilutions of their own pee – and report good results. Apparently, no telltale flavours remain in the produce, either. But is pee really good for plants?

While the use of human faeces on the garden is not recommended for health reasons, the urine from a clean and healthy person is free of any potentially harmful enteric bacteria such as *E. coli*.

On a larger scale, the experience of farmers who opt to use this simple, low-cost fertiliser is positive, resulting in good crops and healthy soil. There is not much enthusiasm internationally, though, for more widespread methods of collection and distribution: the technology for urine-separating lavatories exists, but often they do not reconcile with official building or sanitary regulations. This is a pity.

A Urine contains nitrogen, phosphorus and potassium, and an adult is reported to secrete 11g nitrogen, 1g phosphorus and 2.5g potassium in a single pee. This makes it a balanced and potentially valuable fertiliser.

In Sweden, where separated lavatories are more popular than in many other countries, storage tanks that conserve 3cm² per person are popular, and, come spring, they are emptied onto agricultural land to fertilise crops.

SHOULD I PEE IN MY COMPOST HEAP?

There are good reasons to add pee to compost. The extra nitrogen will enhance the speedy rotting of woody, carbon-rich material, and the potassium and, to a lesser extent, the phosphorus will enhance the nutrient content of the resulting compost. The existing microbes in the compost will render the urine inoffensive quite quickly. If, however, compost becomes on the wet side, it will need extra additions of straw to keep things balanced and the composting process productive.

Why is there moss growing on the lawn?

MOSS IS BRILLIANTLY ADAPTED to growing in damp shade. And while strong, thick grass will suppress moss by shading it and taking all the soil moisture for itself, if a lawn gets trampled and the soil compacted, the result will be a friendly environment for moss – which may grab the opportunity to overrun the lawn grass and take over.

Moss and grass need different circumstances to flourish. If the weather is damp and the grass has been heavily used, the resulting conditions may turn moss into a serious contender for lawn space.

Moss is nature's way of covering soil in places that are too ill-drained and shady for other plants.

A lot of gardeners, especially those keen on smooth, bright green swathes of lawn, fight a long-term battle with moss. Their tactics include spiking lawns in order to aerate the soil (the process is exactly as it sounds, using either solid spikes to make numerous holes in the soil, or hollow spikes that remove thin cores of soil), and feeding the grass to encourage it to outcompete its rival. Moss also prefers an acid soil, so, if lime is added to the lawn to raise the pH, it can encourage grass to grow.

If you can't beat them...

Moss reproduces and spreads by means of spores – and wherever conditions favour moss, it will establish and start growing. Many gardens in damp climates have areas of shade where it is impractical or outright impossible to create favourable growing conditions for grass. When this is the case, the gardener may as well admit defeat and decide to cultivate moss rather than grass as a 'lawn'. This means a reversal of tactics: in a moss

◀ Common haircap moss, *Polytrichum commune*, is widespread and has charming, starry, green foliage.

lawn, grass is the 'weed' and needs to be kept down with targeted weedkillers (moss itself is impervious to most weedkillers). And while there is no need to feed or mow, a moss lawn must be kept damp to flourish. Moss will not stand trampling, either, so a successful moss lawn should have a stepping-stone path so that it can be walked over without damage.

MOSS: THE GREAT SURVIVOR

Moss is a plant, but it lacks both roots and the internal vessels that conduct water. This means that it has to live in a wet environment and will need water to reproduce. Despite these limitations, mosses are amazingly good at exploiting niche environments where there is too little soil for rooted plants (on roofs, for example) or too little light (in shaded woodlands, for example). Moss, therefore, 'greens' the most unpromising environments and plays a valuable part in garden diversity. And although it dries up and can look quite sad and brown in prolonged dry spells, it absorbs water speedily when the rains return, springing back to life in just a few hours. Because of its absorbency, dried sphagnum moss, which can absorb up to 20 times its volume in liquid, was a popular, if rather rough-and-ready, dressing for wounds during the First World War.

**Small red peat moss,
*Sphagnum capillifolium***

What is the difference between a slug and a snail?

SLUGS AND SNAILS HAVE A LOT OF SIMILARITIES: they are both molluscs, the group that also contains shellfish, and both can survive only in moist or wet places. Both are also found in high numbers – sometimes extraordinarily high numbers – in almost any garden, where they are not usually welcome visitors. However, they live rather different lifestyles.

Day-to-day life for slugs and snails

In hot weather, snails avoid drying out by finding a hidden corner and taking shelter within their shells; slugs, meanwhile, are brilliantly engineered to slide and squeeze themselves into the soil. This is why you will usually be able to spot far more snails than slugs out in the garden in daytime. Visit after dark, with a torch, and you will find that the slugs have emerged from their underground shelters and are out in quite as high numbers as snails.

Although snails tend to stay in moist, sheltered areas and avoid the

The obvious visible difference is that a snail has a shell and a slug does not. While the snail's shell can be used as a self-contained shelter, the slug has to find its own protection – and this leads it to spend quite a lot of its time underground.

sun, they are fast to take advantage of rainy weather and can climb very high – it is not unusual to find them at the topmost point of a tall and tasty plant, for example.

Both slugs and snails will use slime in an attempt to avoid being eaten. They can exude it in huge quantities, and it is distasteful to many species of animals.

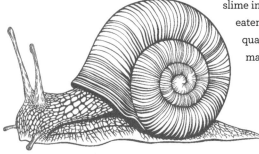

SLUG ANATOMY

They may look rather formless at a glance, but slug anatomy is surprisingly sophisticated.

The head has two pairs of telescopic tentacles, one of which serves as the slug's 'eyes' and the other as its 'nose'. The mouth has rather thick lips, which are drawn back when the slug is feeding; inside is the radula, a tongue-like organ that is covered with rows of teeth that are rough enough to rasp away a leaf's surface when the slug eats. Behind the mouth is a slime gland, which exudes mucus to help the slug slide along.

The mantle is made from thicker skin than the rest of the body. It also contains the slug's breathing cavity – the pneumostome, a breathing pore on the right side of the mantle, opens and closes to let air in and out. Like humans, slugs have a diaphragm, a muscular layer at the base of the breathing cavity that helps to pump air in and out. And the slug can withdraw the rest of its body under the protective mantle if danger threatens. In the case of snails, the mantle is covered by the snail's shell.

The trunk is under the mantle, and contains most of the slug's organs: the heart, a kidney (slugs have just one), and its digestive and reproductive system. Slugs are hermaphrodites: when they want to mate, they wrap themselves around each other and exchange sperm through their protruded genitals.

The 'foot' actually comprises the whole underside of the slug. It is almost entirely formed of muscle; as it contracts and relaxes, it pushes the slug forward. Slugs can only travel in one direction – there is no reverse gear.

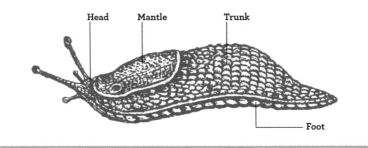

Head   Mantle   Trunk   Foot

Where do bees go in winter?

IT ALL DEPENDS ON THE TYPE OF BEE. The average British garden has between six and ten different species of bee as visitors in a typical summer. These are usually a mix of honeybees, which live in hives; bumblebees, which group together in small colonies; and solitary bees, which, as their name suggests, live alone.

Seeing out the cold season

Honeybees need food in winter, and will either dip into their honey stores, or, if the beekeeper has removed their honey, will nourish themselves on the bee candy or sugar solution they have been left in return. In frigid temperatures, the clustered bees will vibrate their wing muscles to keep warm.

Bumblebees, by contrast, live in underground nests, largely populated by infertile female workers. As winter approaches, both fertile females and males hatch out and leave the nest.

In winter, honeybees remain in their hives, where they cluster together for warmth. Queen bumblebees shelter individually underground, while solitary bees make shelters for themselves where they take cover until warmer temperatures return.

The infertile females in the abandoned colony will die as summer ends. The queen bees will be fertilised shortly after leaving the nest, after which the males also die. The queens are pregnant and have been well nourished to see them through the winter. They shelter individually underground, where they hibernate until spring.

Solitary bees, meanwhile, have neither colony nor hive to concern them. These efficient, little pollinators sit out winter in dugouts or tunnels, emerging in spring to start a cycle of feeding and reproduction as the weather warms.

Western honey bee,
Apis mellifica

Do lawns have to be made of grass?

GRASS IS THE FIRST THING WE THINK OF when we hear the word 'lawn'. Grass is a great surface that works for games and entertaining, or simply for lying about on. Grasses have evolved to withstand the predations of grazing animals, which makes maintenance comparatively easy (although the 'bowling-green' finish of a devoutly tended lawn will always be hard to maintain).

Two traditional alternatives

Camomile lawns have been a favoured option in Atlantic Europe for at least the last four centuries. Camomile, *Chamaemelum nobile*, is a low-growing, evergreen perennial. It is a deep, rich green and smells delicious when crushed, but will not withstand much use – it will need stepping-stones if it is to be regularly walked across. The dwarf, flowerless cultivar 'Treneague' works best for lawn making.

Clover lawns are particularly easy to grow, as many clovers, *Trifolium*, have a naturally creeping habit, resistant to grazing and mowing. Clover has one big advantage in that it is naturally sustainable – it can gather nitrogen from the air and, therefore, needs only a minimal amount of phosphorus and potassium fertiliser.

Grass is not the only plant that can make a lawn – some other low-growing plants can be pressed into service. But the alternative options, while beautiful, are not usually as hardy as a grass lawn.

Its one major disadvantage is that certain pests and diseases can make soil 'clover sick', making it impossible for clover to grow healthily.

Grass lawns have also come under fire recently because of their lack of biodiversity and their high environmental cost in terms of fertilising, mowing and watering. The gardener of the future may turn to an alternative: mixed communities of low-growing plants that do not call for much care, promote biodiversity and are attractive to wildlife.

◀ Low-growing mat-forming thymes, such as *Thymus serpyllum*, make charming, fragrant, flowering carpets.

What is a bird's favourite food?

WHAT FOOD DOES A BIRD LIKE BEST? Well, as you would expect, that depends on the bird. The British Trust for Ornithology has done some studies that illustrate the value of feeding a range of foods to cater for the differing needs of different species, requirements that change with the seasons.

It's all in the beak

A narrow, short beak like a blue tit's is perfect for picking up insects, while a sparrow has a short, broad beak, designed for picking out seeds and grain and pulling them apart to get to the kernel. Starlings, on the other hand, are especially flexible about what they eat and have beaks that look almost spring-loaded in action. When the soil is soft and damp, they stick their beaks in the ground, open them to make a gap, then peer into the hole to check if there are any good worms or grubs to be had. When the ground hardens in winter and the beak-holing method becomes impractical, starlings turn to berries, nuts and grains for their diet.

Wild garden birds (we are not talking about emus or vultures here) eat a wide range of foods. Most cannot afford to be too choosy, but you can see a clue to the food they are best evolved to eat in the shape of their beaks.

Gourmet bird treats

Given all this, it is not surprising that birds will find a wide range of foods palatable on the bird table. Special treats you could offer might include sunflower hearts (easier to access than hard-husked sunflower seeds and full of oil and protein), mealworms (the larvae of the mealworm beetle, available dried or fresh from pet stores) or birdseed balls (a delectable mix of fat and seeds that very few birds can resist).

House sparrow,
Passer domesticus

HOW TO MAKE A BIRDSEED BALL

Make these up as they are needed (they are better fresh) and you can look forward to welcoming a wide range of avian visitors to your garden.

You will need:

• A mixture of all or any of the following dry ingredients. Unsalted broken peanuts, canary seed, dried fruit, dried mealworms (you can buy these in pet stores), muesli, raw porridge oats, sunflower hearts, walnut pieces

• Lard or suet

• Empty plastic tubs or yoghurt pots (use the thin ones so that they can be 'cracked' off the birdseed balls).

• String

Broken-up peanuts

Dried mealworm larvae

1 Prepare two plastic tubs or pots by piercing a small hole in the base, small enough to hold a piece of string tightly.

2 Cut a piece of string around 1m long, feed one end through the hole in the base of the pot and knot it tightly on the outside.

3 Melt the lard or suet in a pan over a low heat.

4 Remove the pan from the heat, then mix in the dry ingredients. The result should have enough fat to bind the dry ingredients into a solid mass.

5 Press the mixture into the pots, around the string, and leave in the fridge to firm up.

6 When the mixture has hardened, cut or crack the plastic pots and pull the birdseed balls out.

7 Hang them up in the garden, using the strings to suspend them by.

Make sure you have water nearby, too, so that the birds can drink as well as feed.

Q Why is my compost hot?

A WARM COMPOST HEAP IS A HAPPY COMPOST HEAP: heat leads to better compost, produced at a faster rate. The breaking down of woody material releases energy just as burning wood in a fire does, although the 'burning' happens much more slowly, and is chemical – resulting from microorganisms exuding enzymes, rather than from direct combustion.

Mercifully, compost heaps do not usually get hot enough to combust and burst into flame. Getting the right mix to their contents is crucial to ensure that they are busily producing a great result. Straw and fallen leaves both work well in either a heap or a compost bin, and too much woody material should be avoided. The mix needs some moisture and some nitrogen to get going; the best mix should typically be around 20 or 30 parts of carbon to each part of nitrogen (hay has around this ration naturally, so is always a great compost addition, but straw is about 80 parts carbon to one part nitrogen, while grass clippings are around 19 parts carbon per nitrogen part). Blended content – not too high in any single ingredient – tends to make the best compost, and it is also useful if you are able to put everything on the compost heap or in the compost bin at the same time; this will help to maintain the heat. If compost seems to be 'going' very slowly, you can dig out the whole heap or empty the bin, mix it thoroughly and then put it back.

A When microorganisms get to work on the carbon-rich organic material in compost, they generate heat. Mild though natural oxidation might seem, it can raise the internal temperature quite high.

The mixing will rekindle the heat of decomposition in the compost and give it a nudge to speed up the process.

Composting bugs

Different kinds of bacteria and microorganisms are working in your compost bin at different times. While the compost is cool, the same bacteria and fungi that undertake the rotting in your garden are at work; as it heats up, though, mesophilic bacteria (those that are able to function at 21–32°C take over and, if the temperature continues to rise, thermophilic bacteria (active at 40– 90°C) will leap into action.

MAKING A HOT BED

In the days before heated greenhouses were common, Victorian gardeners used the natural heat generated by hot beds to grow early crops of cucumber, lettuce and radishes, and sometimes to encourage tender crops such as melons.

Cantaloupe melon,
Cucumis melo

If you want to try out a hot bed for yourself, you will need a cold frame and a clear area of ground slightly larger than the frame. The base of the hot bed needs to be 1m high, and made from a mix of straw, raked leaves and manure. Once in place, leave it to rot (at first, it will smell strongly of ammonia, but it will soon settle down to a warm ferment, which smells much more agreeable). When it has mixed and rotted, and smells merely 'earthy' rather than ripe, add a 30cm layer of of soil on top of it. This is the planting layer. Sow the seeds or small plants you want to grow into it, and place the cold frame over the top. With the right crop, the natural warmth of the bed beneath the soil should ensure rapid and healthy growth.

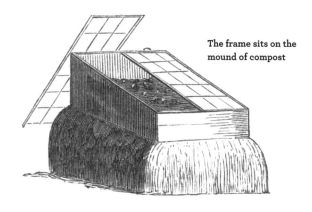

**The frame sits on the
mound of compost**

Q Does beer get rid of slugs?

SLUGS LOVE BEER. This is not because they like alcohol – non-alcoholic beers have been shown to appeal to them just as strongly – it is because the scent and flavour of fermenting yeasts and sugars attracts them. They are also keen on the scent and taste of fermenting fruit.

Using beer traps

Beer traps make use of the slug's natural desire for dark, moist shelter and the presence of fermenting materials – you can either make your own or buy them ready-made. There does not seem to be any particularly effective design; they all work in the same way, by tempting the slug to enter a vessel with some beer at the bottom, from which they cannot escape and in which they ultimately drown. In theory, if you use enough traps, the slug population will be sufficiently reduced for your garden to enjoy the benefit, but, in practice, it is unclear whether this ever really happens. You can use beer traps to get an indication of how bad your slug problem really is, though – and if it is worse than you feared, you can use a more lethal control measure, such as introducing parasitic nematodes to your soil.

A Beer does not seem to do slugs any harm, so as a control measure it is not particularly useful. However, it can be put in slug traps, which both gets rid of the slug and ensures it dies a relatively painless death.

DO SLUGS HAVE BEER PREFERENCES?

A research experiment in America found that slugs seem to like some beers less than others. Budweiser seemed to be significantly less attractive to slugs than other brands, possibly because the chemicals associated with fermentation can differ quite a lot beer-to-beer. If a simple slug trap is too boring for you, try testing the efficacy of different beers in slug entrapment.

How can you tell if pond water is unhealthy?

NATURALLY FORMED PONDS tend to be healthy and well balanced unless they have been contaminated by pollutants or have overly high levels of nutrients. Wind on the water's surface adds oxygen, and the oxygenated water supports an ecosystem that is self-sustaining and keeps the water healthy. Man-made ponds, on the other hand, tend to suffer from man-made problems.

Symptoms of sick water

If fish are dying in a garden pond, it is often a problem with the water and not the fish. If a pond is not deep enough, it can cause stress to fish, but a test-kit or a specialist pond adviser can suggest how to keep the water fish-friendly.

Too much pond algae or duckweed, *Lemna*, is another sign that the water is suffering. Remedial measures can include reducing the fish population, growing more floating surface plants to 'shade out' algae, and avoiding the use of fertiliser near the pond's edges. It can also indicate that a pond is too shallow. This last problem is not so easily solved. Ponds are often made with formers that have a set depth. If problems recur, it may be worth considering removing the liner and digging the pond deeper.

At certain times of year, ponds may appear to be lifeless. This can be seasonal – ponds in winter are often dark and apparently dead – but may also be a sign that something is wrong. Excessive quantities of decaying leaves

An excessive amount of pond algae or duckweed, *Lemna*, growing in a pond indicates that the water is not in a healthy state. Dying fish is another symptom of unhealthy water, and low biological activity on the whole is usually a warning sign.

can cause temporary lifelessness (and it is worth fishing some of them out); shade, too, is not good for pond life, and ponds set in shade can be rather low in biological activity.

▶ The dwarf waterlily, *Nymphaea candida*, can thrive in barrels and tubs as well as ponds, where it can shade out unsightly algae.

How do you attract butterflies?

BUTTERFLIES ARE WELCOME VISITORS TO THE GARDEN.
Highly mobile, they are constantly seeking food plants on which to lay their eggs. And to get about, they need plenty of aviation fuel in the form of sugary flower nectar. A butterfly-friendly garden is not hard to achieve: make a study of the plants they prefer, and you are virtually guaranteed good results.

It is not all botanical glamour. Plants we look on as weeds are sometimes exceptionally attractive to butterflies. If you have a shady corner where weeds will not be too disruptive, you might want to consider cultivating a patch of stinging nettles, *Urtica dioca*.

The best way to attract butterflies is to grow a wide range of nectar-rich plants. Different species favour different flowers, so the wider the choice you offer, the more different butterflies are likely to turn up.

They have a strong appeal to several species, including peacock, red admiral, comma and small tortoiseshell butterflies. Holly blue butterflies, meanwhile, feed on ivy, *Hedera*.

The downside

When the butterfly or moth eggs hatch and the caterpillars emerge, they will occasionally do serious damage to their host plants. The migratory painted lady has form in this behaviour, laying waste to helichrysum (the popular, silver-leaved bedding plant) in some years before heading off back to north Africa. The damage is rarely fatal, however, and should ideally be tolerated. Butterfly and moth numbers have fallen by about 75 per cent over the last 40 years, and these beautiful and important creatures need all the help they can get.

For the same – protective – reason, never spray insecticides onto plants in flower, or where the pesticide fallout could reach nearby flowering plants, including weeds; they can be fatal to butterflies.

Butterfly bush,
Buddleja davidii

BUTTERFLY FAVOURITES

The top 13 plants for maximum
butterfly satisfaction:

- Blackberry, *Rubus fruticosus*

- Butterfly bush, *Buddleja davidii*

- Dahlias (single-flowered), *Dahlia*

- Garden mint, *Mentha spicata*

- Golden rod, *Solidago*

- Heather, *Calluna vulgaris*

- Heaths (a form of heather),
  Erica, Daboecia cantabrica

- Ice plant, *Sedum spectabile*

- Lavender, *Lavandula*

- Masterwort, *Astrantia major*

- Mexican hyssop,
  Agastache foeniculum

- Thyme, *Thymus*

- Purple top, *Verbena bonariensis*

A tip for the lazy gardener
who hates weeding is that,
satisfyingly, dandelions,
Taraxacum officinale, are
rich in nectar, and
butterflies love them.

Heather,
Calluna vulgaris

Dahlia,
Dahlia

Masterwort,
Astrantia major

**Swallowtail, *Papilio machaon*, sitting
on a dandelion, *Taraxacum officinale***

Q How long will a slug take to get back to my garden?

SLUGS ARE DIFFICULT TO TRACK. They move at night, often underground, and it is hard to differentiate one slug from another. So the question of whether or not a slug taken (or perhaps, given how gardeners feel about slugs, flung), 20m away from its home ground would return is a tough one to answer.

A Despite the difficulty of slugs as subjects, ingenious scientists working with captive slugs have found that they can move 4–12m per night, depending on how hungry they are and the condition of the ground they are travelling on.

Slug and snail, tortoise and hare?

Slugs are much slower than snails. In comparative experiments, snails travelled at least twice as fast as slugs (is this perhaps why we say 'sluggish' rather than 'snailish'?). Having fixed, more or less, on the pace at which slugs travel, the next thing to look at is whether they actually want to come back to where they started from.

Slugs have not been established as having any particular association with specific territories (many, though not all, snails, by contrast, often seem to possess a natural homing instinct), so, even if they could return, they might not want to. They do, though, seem to prefer to follow the slime trails left by other molluscs, and this may be an indication that they will return to an area where there are plenty of other slugs and which is, therefore, likely to offer favourable conditions.

◀ Slugs are very variable and identifying each species requires in-depth, microscopic examination of their reproductive organs.

Do brandling worms taste bad?

WE HAVE ALL SEEN BLACKBIRDS AND ROBINS in the garden eating earthworms with apparent relish, so why, if there is an excess of brandling worms (the long, thin, red worms that are the mainstay of compost bins and wormeries) – and a few are left out on the bird table, do birds seem to scorn them?

Self-defence

Even the Latin name of brandling worms, *Eisenia foetida*, implies that they smell bad, and it makes sense for compost-dwelling worms to have a means of defending themselves, as composting material is soft, loose and easily excavated by birds or other predators. Yet birds do not usually disturb compost heaps, while turf or open soil rich in chafer grubs, earthworms, leatherjackets and

Short of conducting a taste test, it is hard to know if brandling worms taste bad. But it is known that they excrete a foul-smelling liquid if they are handled roughly, probably as a defence mechanism, and this may be why birds do not seem to enjoy them.

wireworms is well visited by both birds and animals such as badgers, which are happy to root for such delicacies. The verdict has to be that brandling worms do not taste good enough to be worth hunting for.

MAKING BRANDLINGS PALATABLE

Brandling worms are used as a protein-rich food for chickens, pigs and other farm livestock. However, they have been processed: washed, boiled, dried and ground – and presumably this will have removed any unpleasant-tasting compounds. It is possible that all it would take to make them palatable to wild birds is a good wash. Next time the compost bin or wormery has an excess, it might be worth a try.

Do my fruit trees really need pruning?

ALL TREES HAVE A NATURAL INCLINATION to flower and go on to fruit, and, even without any pruning at all, fruit tree owners would still get a crop. However, a lack of pruning and other general care can lead to highly irregular cropping – and careless pruning can result in odd or irregular cropping patterns.

Trees in the wild

When they are not cultivated, but simply grown in the wild, trees adopt all kinds of strategies to set seed, and these include some that would definitely be unappreciated by fruit growers. Among them are cropping in abundance one year followed by a very sparse crop the next; a tendency to grow too tall (to shade-out competing vegetation); and the habit of producing a large number of very small fruit instead of a smaller number of larger ones.

When trees are grown in cultivation, they can retain some of the characteristics they had in the wild, partly because they are very slow growing compared with smaller plants. It can take as long as 25 years for a fruit tree to be measured and selected, and suitable crosses made, and another 25 years to assess the value of these crosses. All the while, fruit trees are not moving far from their wild relatives in their habits.

Pruning is designed to counter those superfluous survival tactics that are not needed in the orchard; once the tree is in cultivated conditions, it is the grower's responsibility, not the tree's, to protect it from competition and ensure that it has the means to reproduce. And pruning is almost always required to get the best from fruit trees.

Considered pruning is definitely valuable, directing a tree's energy towards regular and heavy cropping – but it is one of those processes that tends to make inexperienced growers very nervous.

When cutting all but the thinnest shoots, professional gardeners favour pruning saws for a clean cut with minimum effort in tight spaces.

GOOD PRUNING PRACTICE

Large fruit trees are kept open and fruitful by sawing out a proportion of the old branches each year. This ensures a constant supply of vigorous branches in uncongested conditions. In turn, these will bear larger fruits ripening in plenty of accessible sunlight to reach the best colour and flavour.

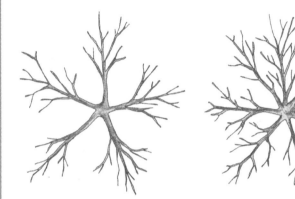

Aim for this...   **... rather than this.**

When the size of trees needs to be reduced, this is usually done by summer pruning. Cutting away strong, green shoots depletes the tree's resources and thus curbs its growth. Summer pruning can also be used to counter a tendency to grow leafy shoots and promote the production of flower buds instead. Excessive flowering, on the other hand, can be countered by cutting out some of the flowering shoots in spring and thus avoiding the feast/famine cycle of years of abundance followed by years of light cropping.

Apple, *Malus*, and pear, *Pyrus*, trees are usually comparatively hard work in pruning terms because the production of such large and resource-costly fruits puts them under strain. Trees that bear smaller fruits, such as cherries and plums, *Prunus*, typically call for a much lighter pruning regime.

Q Does rust spread?

IF YOUR GARDEN TOOLS were not carefully cleaned and oiled before they were put away for the winter, you may find that rust is the unwelcome result when you take them out again in spring. Not only that, but, when one tool gets rusty, it can seem to have spread to all the others.

Rust is a reaction of iron and oxygen in the presence of water. The result is the red, powdery deposit that is hydrated iron oxide. Tools are quickly ruined by rust, as the rusted surface expands and starts to flake, leading to erosion of the iron. Pure iron does not rust, but impure iron or iron alloys rust with ease. Other metals, such as aluminium and copper, form a hard-surface oxide layer that protects the underlying metal, while stainless steel, also an iron alloy, is rustproof, but with the drawback that it is not as strong as other steels.

A Despite appearances, rust does not spread. It is a chemical reaction, rather than a biological infection. However, a collection of iron objects in a damp environment will often rust in a way that could easily be mistaken for an outbreak.

How to avoid rust

Most modern garden tools are made from stainless steel, are galvanised (that is, coated with zinc, a metal that does not rust) or are plastic coated, so rust is less of a problem. Tools made from iron or steel should be cleaned and dried after use, and put away in well-ventilated storage. If the surroundings might be damp,

a coating of a mineral oil spray will keep the water away and protect the metal.

There are some other preventative measures available, too. If galvanised or plastic surfaces get damaged, they can be repainted with zinc-rich paint to prevent further deterioration. Other paints that halt rust and allow for repainting are also available.

Why is it that pests eat my favourite plants, but ignore the weeds?

IT IS FRUSTRATING: you have not weeded properly for a week or two, and the garden has plenty of the sort of plant visitors you could do without, such as dandelions, *Taraxacum officinale*, and chickweed, *Stellaria media*. But when you go out to check on your beds, it is your showpiece dahlias that have been reduced to lacy tatters. Why could the local pests not concentrate on those dandelions instead?

Overcoming disease resistance

The reason that weeds are so resistant to pests has been the subject of many scientific experiments. Environmental and health concerns mean that herbicides are becoming less and less acceptable, and, if herbicides cannot be used, a possible solution lies in biological controls. This would mean that an undesirable plant could be infected with a disease or infested with a pest; the challenge is to overcome the resistance of weeds to natural enemies.

By definition, weeds have evolved to survive all kinds of adverse conditions in the garden, and this includes a lack of susceptibility to pests and diseases. That is why they are called weeds.

ALIEN WEEDS AND UNNATURAL ENEMIES

The most promising results come from tests on 'alien' plants that, after many generations away from the predators of their homeland, have reduced resistance. Japanese knotweed, *Fallopia japonica*, for example, is a notorious weed that is kept in check by natural pests and diseases in its home country, but thrives in a new environment in the absence of native controls. Reintroduce a pest from its home environment a few years later, though, and the knotweed is newly vulnerable and succumbs – because it has shed its natural resistance.

Further Reading

Books

Botany for Gardeners
Brian Capon
Timber Press, 2010

RHS Botany for Gardeners:
The Art and Science of Gardening
Explained & Explored
Geoff Hodge
RHS and Mitchell Beazley, 2013

The Chemistry of Plants: Perfumes,
Pigments and Poisons
Margareta Sequin
Royal Society of Chemistry, 2012

Climate and Weather
John Kington,
Collins, 2010

Earthworm Biology
(Studies in Biology)
John A. Wallwork,
Hodder Arnold, 1983

Hartmann & Kester's Plant
Propagation: Principles
and Practices
Fred T. Davies, Robert Geneve,
Hudson T. Hartmann and
Dale E. Kester Pearson, 2013

Insect Natural History
A. D Imms
Bloomsbury/Collins, 1990

Life in the Soil: A Guide for
Naturalists and Gardeners
James B. Nardi
University of Chicago Press, 2007

The Life of a Leaf
Steven Vogel
University of Chicago Press, 2013

The Living Garden
Edward J. Salisbury
G. Bell & Sons, 1943

Mushrooms
Roger Phillips
Macmillan, 2006

Nature in Towns and Cities
David Goole
William Collins, 2014

Nature's Palette:
The Science of Plant Color
David Lee
University of Chicago Press,
2008

Plant Pests
David V. Alford
Collins, 2011

The Secret Life of Trees:
How They Live and Why
They Matter
Colin Tudge
Penguin Books, 2006

Science and the Garden:
The Scientific Basis of
Horticultural Practice
Peter J. Gregory, David S. Ingram
and Daphne Vince-Prue (Eds.)
Wiley-Blackwell, 2016

Trees: Their Natural History
Peter A. Thomas
Cambridge University Press,
2014

Weeds & Aliens
Edward J. Salisbury
Collins, 1961

Journals and articles

'The formation of vegetable mould, through the action of worms, with observations on their habits'
Charles Darwin, 1890
https://archive.org/details/
formationofveget01darw
(Accessed 15 May 2016)

PLOS Biology
http://journals.plos.org/plosbiology/
Open access scientific journal.

Rogers Mushrooms
Roger Phillips
http://www.rogersmushrooms.com
(Accessed 16 May 2016)

DVDs

The Private Life of Plants (DVD)
David Attenborough
2012

Index

Credits